It's Another Ace Book from CGP

It's chock-full of questions that
are carefully designed to cover all the
<u>really important formulas</u> in GCSE Physics.

There are <u>routine</u> questions to make sure you're a dab hand
at <u>rearranging</u> the formulas and sticking numbers in — and then
there are wordier questions like you get in the <u>exam</u>.

Simple as that.

If only someone hadn't spoiled it all by putting in all the daft funny bits.

CGP are just the best

The central aim of Coordination Group Publications is to produce
top quality books that are carefully written, beautifully
presented and marvellously funny — whilst always making sure
they exactly cover the National Curriculum for each subject.

And then we supply them to as many people as we possibly can,
as <u>cheaply</u> as we possibly can.

Buy our books — they're ace

Contents

Contributors:
Dominic Hall BSc (Hons)
Lindsay Jordan BSc (Hons)
Tim Major $^2/_3$ of a BSc (Hons)
Isaac Newton BA (Hons), MA
Claire Thompson BSc
Tim Wakeling BA (Hons), GIMA
James Paul Wallis BEng (Hons)
Suzanne Worthington BSc (Hons)

Published by Coordination Group Publications Ltd.
ISBN 1-84146-407-4
Groovy website: www.cgpbooks.co.uk
Jolly bits of clipart from CorelDRAW
Printed by Elanders Hindson, Newcastle upon Tyne.
With thanks to Colin Wells for the proof-reading
Text, design, layout and original illustrations © Coordination Group Publications Ltd. 2001

Doing Formula Questions

Physics is famed for being hard but once you can do one formula, you can do them <u>all</u>.
OK, they change the letters, but all these formula questions are really asking the <u>same thing</u>.

It <u>doesn't matter</u> <u>what the letters are</u>

$$a=bc \qquad P=IV \qquad F=ma$$

1) Those three formulas <u>look</u> totally different.

2) But when you get given b and c and have to work out a, it's exactly the <u>same</u> as if you're given I and V and have to work out P.

3) Nearly all formula questions are <u>exactly the same</u>, just with <u>different letters</u>.

It's all multiplying or dividing

1) When you're given $a=bc$, there are <u>three</u> things they could ask — "what is a", "what is b" or "what is c".

2) But two of those are <u>exactly the same</u> — you <u>work out b</u> in exactly the same way as you <u>work out c</u>.

3) So there's really only two things they can ask you to work out: <u>two things multiplied</u> or <u>one thing divided by another</u>.

4) And that's all these questions are, just <u>dividing</u> or <u>multiplying</u>.

They're all the <u>same</u> as these examples

| EXAMPLE QUESTION | A toy rocket of mass 0.3 kg has an acceleration of 5 m/s². |

ANSWER: What is the resultant force on it?

1) The quantities are <u>mass</u>, <u>force</u> and <u>acceleration</u>.
2) The formula with those in is $F=ma$ (you can look it up in the table on the inside front cover, but you're going to have to learn it sometime).
3) So put 0.3 in place of m and put 5 in place of a.
4) $F=0.3\times5=1.5\,N$

| EXAMPLE QUESTION | A resultant force of 4.7 N acts on a tiny 1 kg dog. |

ANSWER: What is its acceleration?

1) The quantities are <u>mass</u>, <u>force</u> and <u>acceleration</u>.
2) The formula with those in is $F=ma$, but this time you want to work out a, not F.
3) Rearrange it to get $a=F\div m$.
4) Stick 4.7 in for F and 1 in for m.
5) $a=4.7\div1=4.7\,m/s^2$

Check your answers <u>aren't ridiculous</u>

1) If you had a question about the <u>height of a person</u>, and your answer was <u>3000 m</u>, chances are you've <u>screwed up</u>.
2) You might have <u>multiplied</u> instead of <u>dividing</u>, or got your <u>units</u> wrong somewhere.
3) If you get something like 3000 m or 0.0000012 as an answer, <u>check it again</u>.
4) You'd have to be pretty <u>confident</u> to leave something like that as your <u>final answer</u>.

The opposite of juggling — looks hard, but it's easy...

Blimey — so it's actually <u>easy</u>, then. Seems like a con — physics is <u>supposed</u> to be hard.
That's what I thought anyway. But once you know what <u>formula</u> you've got to use, you just <u>stick the numbers in</u> instead of the letters, and either <u>multiply</u> or <u>divide</u>. After you realise that, it's easy.

See p8–9 (Higher) or p13–15 (Foundation) of our Revision Guide

The Secret of Formula Triangles

Remembering formulas is easy as long as you bother to <u>learn them</u> — and multiplying and dividing are a push-over, so the only bit left is <u>rearranging</u> the formulas. And this page makes that easy too.

Use a <u>formula triangle</u> <u>if you want to get it right</u>

Formula triangles make doing formula question about 137 times easier.
And practically every formula in Physics goes into one.

1) If the formula is "A=B×C" then A goes on the <u>top</u> and B×C goes on the <u>bottom</u>.

2) If the formula is "A=B/C" then B must go on <u>top</u> (because it's the only way you can get <u>B divided</u> by something), so A and C go on the bottom.

| EXAMPLES |

$V=I\times R$
becomes:

$F=ma$
becomes:

$F=W/d$
becomes:

Using Formula Triangles — Three Steps

1) Write down the thing you <u>want</u>, and put '=' after it.
2) In the triangle, cover up the thing you want to find, and write down <u>what's left showing</u>.
3) You've now got the <u>formula</u> — <u>stick the numbers in</u> and you're done.

| EXAMPLES |

1) To find W from the 3rd triangle, <u>cover up</u> W and you get F×d.
So W=F×d.

2) To find m from the 2nd one, <u>cover up</u> m, and write down the rest: F/a.
So m=F/a.

...so I used the formula triangle and proved 1 + 1 = 2!

| EXAMPLE QUESTION |

A bulb is connected to a 15 V battery. The bulb has resistance of 30 W.
What current flows through it?

ANSWER:

1) You've got <u>voltage</u> and <u>resistance</u>, and you want <u>current</u>.
So the formula you need is V=IR.

2) Put it into a <u>formula triangle</u> (V on top):

3) <u>Cover up</u> what you're after (I) and <u>write down</u> what you get: I=V/R

4) <u>Stick the numbers</u> in and there you go: I=15/30=0.5 A

5) Check it's <u>sensible</u> — it's not 50 000 A or 0.00000765436 A.

That's it — easy once you've learnt it.

<u>Take 2 equations into the exam? Not me, I just rearrange and go...</u>

2 short pages, one big message — it's <u>nowhere near as hard</u> as it's cracked up to be. There are 3 things you've got to do: remember all these formula questions are the <u>same thing</u>, learn how to use a <u>formula triangle</u>, and do the <u>hard grind</u> of learning the formulas. Then you'll get them <u>all right</u>.

See p9 (Higher) or p14—15 (Foundation) of our Revision Guide

The Secrets of Units and Formulas

Checking units is a real pain in the neck. But the alternative is getting the answer wrong, which is even worse. It's one of life's little niggles that you have to put up with.

Check your units before you start the sums

1) Make sure the units you put into the formula are standard (SI) units.
2) If the question gives you mass in grams, change it to kg before you use it.
3) If you don't put standard units in, there's no way you can get standard units out.
4) And if your answer isn't in standard units, it'll be wrong, plain and simple.
5) Unless they specifically ask for it in some other unit, in which case you pretty obviously have to use the one they ask for.

Give your answer in the right units

1) In the exam, they normally give you the units.
2) But you still need to check them.
3) Make sure the units you've used are the same as the ones they want.
4) Don't put time in minutes if they have it in hours. Or length in cm if they use metres.

The 'Units Trick' for Speed and Electricity Used

1) This is a great trick that works for s=d/t, P=F/A and E=Pt (electricity used=power×time).
2) If they give you the units, you can work out the formula.
3) Just write down the most complicated unit (ie the one that's got several bits).
4) Replace each bit of the unit with what that bit would measure.
   (Eg: in N/m², N measures force, m² measures area.)
5) Bingo. What you've written down is the formula.

> That sounds a bit confusing, but look at this example and it'll all become clear:
> **QUESTION:** What's the formula for speed, distance and time?
> **ANSWER:**
> 1) The units are m/s, m and s.
> 2) So write down the unit made up of several bits: speed = m/s
> 3) Change m to distance (because metres measure distance) and change s to time (because seconds measure time).
> 4) You get speed = distance/time or s=d/t.
> 5) Voilà, that's the formula.

You can do the same thing with the formula for pressure, force and area (remember pressure is measured in N/m², which is the same as Pascals) and for the formula for Electricity used, power and time.

For some reason I expected to see two politicians on page 3...

Watch out for those units. The golden rule is **ALWAYS USE STANDARD UNITS**. That way you can't end up with it all getting mixed up. I know I'm going on about it, but it is blummin' important. If you don't bother to get basic stuff like this right, you're going to have real problems later on.

See p8–9 (Higher) or p13–15 (Foundation) of our Revision Guide

Electrical Power

Electrical power is measured in Watts (W) or Kilowatts (kW).

$$P = V \times I$$

Power   Voltage   Current

EG:
Find P if V=240V and I=12A

$$P = 240 \times 12 = 2880 \, W$$

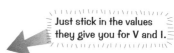

Just stick in the values they give you for V and I.

Q1 Find the power from circuits with these voltages and currents.

a) Voltage 6 V, current 3 A

b) Voltage 8 V, current 2 A

c) V = 9 V, I = 3 A

d) Voltage 3 V, current 3 A

e) V = 12 V, I = 0.2 A

f) Voltage 12 V, current 1.4 A

g) Voltage 9 V, current 2.5 A

h) V = 1.25 V, I = 4 A

i) Voltage 5.13 V, current 10 A

You need to rearrange the formula for the next questions. Have a look at page 2 for the easy way to do it. Then just stick the numbers in.

Q2 Find the voltage of appliances with these power values and currents.

You need the power in Watts, not Kilowatts.

a) P = 10 W, I = 2 A

b) P = 5 W, I = 2 A

c) P = 17 kW, I = 850 A

d) P = 8 kW, I = 16 A

e) P = 9 W, I = 4 A

f) P = 10 kW, I = 200 A

g) P = 5 kW, I = 4 A

h) P = 10 kW, I = 16 A

i) P = 225 W, I = 6 A

Rearrange the formula again and stick in the numbers.

Q3 Find the current flowing through appliances with these power and voltage values.

a) Power 10 kW, voltage 200 V

b) P = 14 kW, V = 7 V

c) Voltage 12 V, power 24 kW

d) P = 15 kW, V = 250 V

e) Power 9 kW, voltage 2 V

f) P = 25 W, V = 2 V

g) Voltage 0.5 V, power 55 W

h) P = 2 kW, V = 2.5 V

i) V = 75 V, P = 30 kW

With wordy ones like this you have to read through it to find the letters, then stick it into the formula.

Q4 Francis is using a hairdryer plugged into the mains. It has 230 V across it.

a) Work out the power from the hairdryer if 6 A flows through the circuit.

Most electrical appliances have their power and operating voltage written on them.

b) Work out the power of the hairdryer if 4.6 A flows through the circuit.

c) Work out the current that flows through a hairdryer with 30 V across it, if it gives 300 W.

Hint — the fuse should be a round number, slightly higher than the normal current.

d) Francis has another hairdryer rated at 120 V, 1.4 kW. Find the fuse needed for the circuit.

Electrical power — you can't lick it...

Better get used to this formula, it's like all the ones in this book — easy to remember, but not the most fascinating thing in the world. The Electrical Power formula is one of the easiest — make sure you've got it stuffed into your brain, or you won't have much chance with all the others.

See p64 (Higher) or p63 (Foundation) of our Revision Guide

Electrical Power

Electrical power questions crop up all the time in exams. There's only three things
they can ask you — find P, find I or find V. It's only easy if you know the formula...

Q1   A treadmill has a power output of 1.5 kW.

a) If a current of 10 A flows, what is the
voltage rating of the treadmill?

b) What voltage would be across the
treadmill if the current was 12 A?

c) What voltage would be across the
treadmill if the current was 6 A?

*Remember to use
a fuse with a
value above the
normal current in
the circuit.*

d) What kind of fuse would be needed if the voltage rating of the treadmill was 600 V?

Q2   A computer running off the mains has 230 V across it.

a) What's the power of the computer if 5.2 A flows through it?

b) If 6.1 A flows through the computer, how much power is there?

c) What value of fuse should be used if the power from the computer is 500 W?

d) What fuse would be needed if the power from the computer was 2.15 kW?

e) If the computer is run from a cyclo-generator, which gives 200 V, and the current
flowing is 4 A, what would the power be?

f) If the computer's still being driven by the cyclo-generator, and the power is 500 W,
what current would be flowing?

Q3   An electric piano has a power value of 600 W.

a) The voltage of mains electricity is 230 V.
What current flows through the piano at this voltage?

b) If a current of 5 A flows, what's the voltage
across the piano?

c) Would you use a 20 A or a 30 A fuse if
the voltage across the piano was 24 V?

d) Would you use a 35 A or a 40 A fuse
if the voltage across the piano was 16 V?

I'm an electrifying cook — my current buns are to die for...

Sometimes you'll get a question about P=I²R. It looks complicated, but it's just what you get
when you combine P=IV and R=V/I. Work out V by using R=V/I (see p.6) and then stick it into
P=IV, that's my advice. Saves you learning another formula. So don't panic if you see P=I²R.

See p64 (Higher) or p63 (Foundation) of our Revision Guide (that's just in case you haven't read page 4...)

Resistance

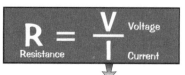

$$R = \frac{V}{I}$$

R = Resistance, V = Voltage, I = Current

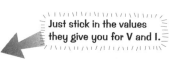

Just stick in the values they give you for V and I.

EG:
Find R if V = 240 V and I = 15 A

$$R = 240 \div 15 = 16\ \Omega$$

Q1 Work out the resistance of bulbs with these voltages and currents.

Resistance tells you how much current a component allows to flow through it.

a) V = 6 V, I = 3 A
b) V = 8 V, I = 2 A
c) V = 9 V, I = 3 A
d) V = 3 V, I = 3 A
e) V = 12 V, I = 2 A
f) V = 12 V, I = 4 A
g) V = 9 V, I = 2 A
h) V = 1 V, I = 4 A
i) V = 5 V, I = 10 A

Q2 Work out the voltage across resistors with these resistances and currents.

You'll have to swap the formula around: voltage = current × resistance

Resistance is measured in Ohms, written as Ω.

a) R = 3 Ω, I = 2 A
b) R = 2 Ω, I = 5 A
c) R = 4 Ω, I = 4 A
d) R = 6 Ω, I = 3 A
e) R = 4 Ω, I = 0.5 A
f) R = 18 Ω, I = 0.5 A
g) R = 9 Ω, I = 0.5 A
h) R = 12 Ω, I = 0.25 A
i) R = 1.2 Ω, I = 10 A

Q3 Work out the current through wires with these resistances and voltages.

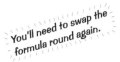

You'll need to swap the formula round again.

a) R = 2 Ω, V = 4 V
b) R = 2 Ω, V = 6 V
c) R = 3 Ω, V = 9 V
d) R = 6 Ω, V = 12 V
e) R = 4 Ω, V = 12 V
f) R = 4 Ω, V = 4 V
g) R = 8 Ω, V = 4 V
h) R = 8 Ω, V = 2 V
i) R = 10 Ω, V = 6 V

Q4 A Physics teacher has wired his talking bear up to a circuit. There are 30 V across it, and the current is 6 A.

a) What is the resistance of the bear?

b) The teacher puts a 12 V battery in the circuit instead of the old one. What's the current now?

Q5 Now the Physics teacher has wired the bear into the mains.

a) What is the current through the bear if its resistance stays the same?

b) What would the current be if he used a 120 V adaptor?

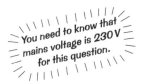

You need to know that mains voltage is 230 V for this question.

Resistance isn't futile, it's very, very useful... © Prof Davros

I bet you love it when you can make one formula into three different ones just by swapping the terms around. Well maybe not — but it means you only need to remember the formula <u>once</u> and then <u>work out</u> the others. And making formulas easy to learn is what makes the world go round.

See page 1 of our Physics Revision Guide

Resistance

There isn't much to exam questions about resistance. If you slog through
all these practice questions, you'll be able to do them in your sleep.

Q1 A special edition belly-dancing stereo has 120 V across it.

a) What is the resistance of the stereo if
there is a current of 5 A through it?

b) If the current through the stereo increases to
8 A, what must the new resistance be?

c) Bruce powers the stereo from a 6 V battery.
If the resistance is now 1.2 Ω, what is the current?

Q2 A circuit has 3 components in series with resistances of 4 Ω, 6 Ω and 2 Ω.

a) What is the total resistance in the circuit?

b) If the circuit is connected to a 24 V battery,
what is the current in the circuit?

Use the TOTAL resistance to work this out.

c) What battery voltage is being used if a current of 0.5 A flows through the circuit?

d) What current (to 1 d.p.) flows through the circuit if it is connected to the mains voltage of 230 V?

Q3 A new lawnmower motor has 18 Ω resistance.

a) What current (to 1 d.p.) flows through the
motor if it runs off 230 V mains electricity?

b) If the lawnmower is unplugged from the mains and is run
off a 30 V battery instead, what current will flow? (1 d.p.)

c) What battery voltage would
allow a 1.5 A current to flow?

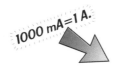

1000 mA = 1 A.

d) Another lawnmower runs off the mains
and allows a current of 6500 mA to flow.
What is its resistance to 1 decimal place?

What makes batteries work in Warsaw? — Pole volts...

Questions on resistance in exams are usually pretty easy, just like the ones on this page. As long
as you don't get the formula the wrong way round, you're laughing. It'll help if you remember
that <u>mains electricity is at **230 V**</u> — and don't forget to keep values in the right units.

See page 1 of our Physics Revision Guide

Energy in Kilowatt-hours

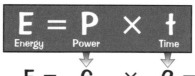

$$E = P \times t$$
Energy   Power   Time

Just shove the values they give you for P and t here.

EG:
Find E if P=6kW and t=2hours

$$E = 6 \times 2 = 12 \text{ kWh}$$

Q1 Work out how much energy (in kWh) is used for each of these periods of time for a 2 kW appliance.

An electricity meter counts the number of units used. Another name for a unit is a kilowatt-hour (kWh or kW-h).

   a) 3 hours   d) 2.5 hours   g) a day

   b) 6 hours   e) 1.5 hours   h) 10 minutes

   c) 12 hours   f) 7.5 hours   i) 6 minutes

You'll need the time in hours.

Q2 Work out the power output of appliances that transfer these amounts of energy in 4 hours.

   a) 8 kWh   d) 2 kWh   g) 46 kWh

   b) 12 kWh   e) 6 kWh   h) 90 kWh

   c) 32 kWh   f) 3 kWh   i) 4.8 kWh

Q3 These appliances of different powers used 6 kWh of energy each. Work out the number of hours that they were used for.

Don't forget to change the power to kW for each calculation.

   a) 6 kW   d) 12 kW   g) 3000 W

   b) 2 kW   e) 24 kW   h) 500 W

   c) 1 kW   f) 8 kW   i) 100 kW

Q4 A cyclist is pedalling an exercise bike to power a huge light bulb. He has a power output of 30 kW.

   a) How much energy will he have used in 3.5 hours?

   b) How much energy will he have used in 15 minutes?

   c) How long can he power the bulb for, if he uses 20 kWh of energy?

   d) The cyclist powers the bulb from a battery because he's tired out. It uses 1152 kWh of energy in two days. What was its power output?

Give me NRG in kWh ASAP SVP...

The important thing to remember on this page is that a __kilowatt-hour is an amount of energy__, not a unit of power. And the best way of figuring out the formula is by remembering the unit — energy is measured in kWh, which means kW×h. So that's one formula you'll have sussed in the exam.

See p11 (Higher) or p12 (Foundation) of our Revision Guide

Cost of Electricity

cost = **units** × **price**
of electricity   of electricity   per unit

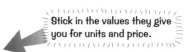
Stick in the values they give you for units and price.

EG:
Find the cost in £ if 100 units are used and a unit costs 8 p

cost = 100 × 0.08 = £8

Q1 Work out the cost (in £) of these amounts of energy if the price of one unit is 7.5 p.

1 kWh=1 unit.

a) 100 kWh
b) 1000 kWh
c) 90 kWh
d) 150 kWh
e) 500 kWh
f) 1600 kWh
g) 516 kWh
h) 998 kWh
i) 34 612 kWh

Q2 Work out the number of units you could pay for with these amounts of money if the price of one unit is 8 p.

Watch it — don't mix up £ and p in questions like this.

a) 80 p
b) £1.60
c) £16.00
d) £80.00
e) £45.00
f) £500.00
g) £750.00
h) £51.80
i) £757.20

Q3 Work out what the cost of one unit of energy was (to the nearest tenth of a penny) if £70.00 bought this number of units.

a) 1000 units
b) 500 units
c) 700 units
d) 750 units
e) 650 units
f) 550 units
g) 825 units
h) 574 units
i) 631 units

Q4 Sherlock is inspecting his electricity meter. The last time he checked, its counter read 564 215.4 units. Now it reads 565 897.5 units.

a) How many units has he used since the last time he checked?

b) One unit costs 8 p. How much will his electricity bill be?

c) Last month, Sherlock paid £210. How many units did he use?

d) Ten years ago, electricity was cheaper. One month, Sherlock paid £130 for 2000 units. How much did one unit cost?

564 897 5

What do electric companies and herons have in common?...
You've got to learn this, and it's useful too, because now you can check your own electricity meter — which is nice. Always make sure you've got <u>both</u> the price per unit <u>and</u> the cost in either <u>pounds</u> or <u>pence</u> before you plug them into the formula, or you'll end up with an answer that's utter rubbish.

See p11 (Higher) or p12 (Foundation) of our Revision Guide

Energy and Cost

Questions in exams often lump different formulas together into one question — so you've got to be able to work out amounts of energy used, and then how much it all costs.

Q1   A hand buzzer has a power output
of 3.5 kW from the battery.

a) For how long had the buzzer been buzzing
by the time 14 kWh of energy had been used?

b) The battery will run out after 7.5 hours of buzzing.
How much energy will it have used by then?

c) A different battery gives 31.5 kWh of energy before it runs out.
How many extra hours of buzzing does this battery provide?

Q2   Cliff's washing machine has a power output of 4.5 kW.

a) How much energy does the washing machine use in 3 hours?

b) If the washing machine has used 15.75 kWh of energy,
how long has the washing machine been in use?

c) Last time he paid a bill, Cliff's electricity meter read
3546237 units. It now reads 3551243 units. If Cliff's
bill this time comes to £300.36, how much is one unit?

*Ouch. There's a lot of bits to this one.
Take each step one at a time.*

Q3   Harold's illuminated jacket has a power output of 2.5 kW.

a) If 3.125 kWh of energy has been used, for how
many minutes has Harold been using the jacket?

b) Harold's plugged his jacket into the mains. How
much energy is used by the jacket in two hours?

c) How much has Harold added to his electricity bill
in two hours, if the price of one unit is 9 p?
*Use the answer to another question to work this out,
and remember Cost=Units×Price.*

d) Harold plugs three jackets into the mains — each with a
power rating of 2.5 kW. How much will he add to his
electricity bill in 3 hours, if the price of one unit is 9 p?

*Lots of parts to this one —
just work it out a bit at a time.*

...they can both stick their bills...

Always remember to have <u>energy in kW</u> and <u>time in hours</u> for these questions. If there's lots of
steps to a question, just figure out what you <u>do</u> know and then work out the rest. And you
shouldn't have too much trouble remembering the formulas — they're pretty obvious, really.

See p11 (Higher) or p12 (Foundation) of our Revision Guide

Force and Motion

$$F = m \times a$$

Force   Mass   Acceleration

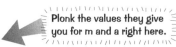

Plonk the values they give you for m and a right here.

EG:
Find F if m=5 kg and a=2 m/s²

$$F = 5 \times 2 = 10\,N$$

Give answers on this page to 1 decimal place where needed.

Q1 Find the force acting on an object with a mass of:

a) 10 kg at 5 m/s²

b) 5 kg at 7 m/s²

c) 94 kg at 4 m/s²

d) 0.75 kg at 3 m/s²

e) 1.26 kg at 1.7 m/s²

f) 38 kg at 5.8 m/s²

g) 58.9 kg at 4.3 m/s²

h) 1237 kg at 6.8 m/s²

i) 0.56 kg at 9.42 m/s²

Q2 What is the acceleration of these masses if the resultant force on them is:

a) 100 N, mass 5 kg

b) 35 N, mass 7 kg

c) 84 N, mass 6 kg

d) 20.4 N, mass 3.2 kg

e) 12.5 N, mass 37.5 kg

f) 4 N, mass 0.64 kg

g) 56 N, mass 2 kg

h) 193 N, mass 49 kg

i) 7.1 N, mass 238 g

Q3 What is the mass of an object if the acceleration and resultant force are:

a) 4 m/s², 40 N

b) 8 m/s², 64 N

c) 2.4 m/s², 92 N

d) 5.2 m/s², 13 N

e) 9.81 m/s², 56 N

f) 2.34 m/s², 43 N

g) 1.2 m/s², 78 N

h) 3.5 m/s², 20.5 N

i) 7.25 m/s², 109 N

Q4 What is the resultant force on these objects?

Use 2 d.p. for parts e, f and g.

a) A car of mass 1200 kg accelerating at 3 m/s².

b) A 14 kg dog running with an acceleration of 1.8 m/s².

c) A scooter and rider with a total mass of 270 kg accelerating at 3.4 m/s².

d) A 200 kg jetski and the 68 kg rider accelerating at 1.2 m/s².

e) A feather of 3 g falling with an acceleration of 7.2 m/s².

f) A 183 kg motorised oven containing a 2.7 kg cake accelerating at 2.56 m/s².

g) A 76 kg skyboarder with his 5 kg board falling with an acceleration of 9.81 m/s².

Force calculations complete them well you must mmmmm.

Force and Motion — what can I say... Learn it.

The <u>resultant</u> force F is the overall <u>unbalanced</u> force. If the forces are balanced then the object moves at constant speed. You need to understand this so it all becomes obvious, then you'll wonder how you got through life without the genius of Newton. (Aaaah — ignorance is bliss...)

See p24 (Higher) or p28 (Foundation) of our Revision Guide

Force and Motion

The best way to get formulas into your head is to do practice question after practice question. That's why, kind soul that I am, I've given you so many.

Q1   Which object has the biggest force acting on it?   *Give your answers to 1 d.p.*

a)   A 5 kg rock accelerating at 3 m/s² or a 7 kg boulder accelerating at 2 m/s².

b)   A 800 kg Mini accelerating at 4 m/s² or a 5000 kg van accelerating at 0.5 m/s².

c)   A 78 kg skier accelerating at 1.6 m/s² or a 83 kg snowboarder accelerating at 1.4 m/s².

d)   A 250 kg motorbike accelerating at 0.75 m/s² or a 20 kg bicycle accelerating at 8 m/s².

e)   A 59 kg skydiver accelerating at 9.81 m/s² or a 63 kg parachutist decelerating at 9 m/s².

f)   A 100 g sparrow accelerating at 1.8 m/s² or a 700 g magpie accelerating at 0.5 m/s².

g)   A 500 kg horse decelerating at 5.5 m/s² or a 180 kg motorbike decelerating at 12 m/s².

Q2   What is the change in acceleration if the force changes from: *Work out the acceleration for both forces, then find the difference.*

a)   10 N to 20 N on a 2 kg mass   e)   40.5 N to 57 N on a 29 kg mass

b)   32 N to 64 N on an 8 kg mass   f)   114 N to 138 N on a 52 kg mass

c)   89 N to 104 N on a 3 kg mass   g)   2.7 N to 4.9 N on a 520 g mass

d)   26 N to 24 N on a 0.25 kg mass   h)   429 N to 786 N on a 780 kg mass

Q3 a) What resultant force does a 30 kg mass need to accelerate at 2.45 m/s²?

b)   A car has a forward thrust of 680 N and a drag of 49 N acts in the opposite direction. What is the resultant force in the forward direction?

c)   A child on a skateboard is accelerating at 2.95 m/s² with a resultant force of 138 N. What is the child's weight to the nearest kilogram if the skateboard has a mass of 1.4 kg?

d)   In a cheese-rolling competition the heaviest cheese is 14 kg. The cheese accelerates at 4.2 m/s². What is the resultant force on it at this acceleration?

e)   The maximum resultant force a fish can generate when swimming is 38 N. What will its acceleration be if the fish weighs 7 kg?

f)   A thief is pulling a woman's bag with a force of 29 N. The woman is trying to get her bag back with a pull of 18.5 N. How heavy is the bag if the acceleration is 1.6 m/s²? Is the bag accelerating towards the woman or the thief?

I'm fed up of these puns — they're all too forced...

F=ma is absolutely fundamental to Physics. It's as famous as E=mc² but with one huge difference — you have to learn F=ma and know how to use it. If you don't get it into your brain, you may as well wave goodbye to several tasty marks. That'd be a shame — it's dead easy really.

See p24 (Higher) or p28 (Foundation) of our Revision Guide

Force and Motion

F = ma doesn't usually get a whole question all to itself. The examiners could chuck in speed, power, energy and anything else that takes their fancy.

Q1   A young farm-hand's tractor won't start so she pushes it along the road to a garage. The tractor has a mass of 340 kg.

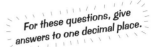
For these questions, give answers to one decimal place.

a) If she pushes the tractor with a resultant force of 860 N, what acceleration will it have?

b) There are several things she can do to decrease the acceleration. Write down two things.

c) The farmer's sheepdog thought it might be fun to sit on the tractor while she pushes. If he has a mass of 17 kg, how much harder will she have to push to get the same acceleration?

d) Would the tractor stop if the girl stopped pushing it and there was no friction at all?

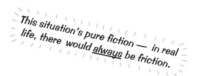
This situation's pure fiction — in real life, there would <u>always</u> be friction.

Q2   A supermarket trolley has a mass of 32 kg. If it's fully loaded, it has a mass of 275 kg.

a) At the start of a trolley dash, what force must an empty trolley be pushed with for it to accelerate at 3 m/s²?

b) If the trolley is full, what force would the trolley have to be pushed with to get the same acceleration?

c) The woman can push the trolley with a maximum force of 800 N. To the nearest kg, what is the maximum mass that the trolley can have if she is to accelerate at 3 m/s²?

Q3   Four men use a snowmobile to travel across ice and snow. It has a mass of 288 kg and the men are 78 kg each on average.

Drag ← → Thrust

a) What force does the full snowmobile exert on the ice when it's standing still?

b) What force does the ice exert on the full snowmobile when it's not moving?

c) The snowmobile moves on the ice with an acceleration of 4.7 m/s². What is the resultant force on the snowmobile and what direction is it in?

There's no acceleration in the up/down direction...

d) The total drag on the snowmobile is 200 N. What is the forward thrust from the engine?

e) The men add a 22 kg jet-pack to the snowmobile. If this adds another 55 N to the forward thrust, what would the new resultant force be if the drag stays the same? What is the new acceleration to one d.p.?

If you reckon this question is easy, sign up for the A-level now...

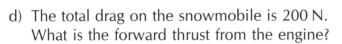
Just think — if Newton had died at birth, these 3 pages wouldn't exist...

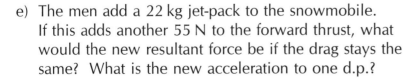
Questions using F=ma crop up all over the place in Physics. Just when you think you're done with using that formula it will pop up again. That's why it's absolutely essential that you know it off by heart. You've got to know how to use it as well — it'd be pretty useless otherwise...

See p24 (Higher) or p28 (Foundation) of our Revision Guide

Mass and Weight

$N = Kg \times N/Kg$

$$W = m \times g$$
Weight   Mass   Pull of Gravity

Just stick in the values they give you for m and g.

EG:
Find W if m=70 kg and g=10 N/kg

$W = 70 \times 10 = 700\,N$

Q1 Work out the weights of these masses on the Earth (where g = 10 N/kg):

a) 5 kg   d) 32.5 kg   g) 0.3 kg

b) 10 kg   e) 0.5 kg   h) 231.5 kg

c) 227 kg   f) 3.5 kg   i) 0.25 kg

Q2 Work out the masses of these weights on the Earth:

a) 6 N   d) 50 N   g) 34 N

b) 8 N   e) 320 N   h) 254 N

c) 143 N   f) 2 N   i) 0.5 N

Sometimes you need the formula the other way round: mass=weight÷g

Q3 Work out what these masses would weigh on the Moon, where g = 1.6 N/kg:

a) 5 kg   d) 32.5 kg   g) 0.3 kg

b) 10 kg   e) 0.5 kg   h) 231.5 kg

c) 227 kg   f) 3.5 kg   i) 0.25 kg

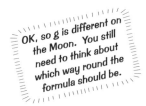

OK, so g is different on the Moon. You still need to think about which way round the formula should be.

Q4 Bob weighs an object with a mass of 12 kg. It weighs 19.2 N.

a) Is he on the Earth or the Moon? How can you tell?

b) Bob (naked) has a mass of 65 kg. How much does he weigh: i) on Earth, ii) on the Moon?

c) When Bob puts his thick coat on, he has a mass of 80 kg.
   How much does he weigh now: i) on Earth, ii) on the Moon?

You'll need information from some of the bits you've already answered.

d) One of Bob's shoes weighs 8 N on the Moon. What is its mass?

e) What is Bob's weight on Earth if wears the coat and a pair of shoes?

Weighty Mass — A heavy-going church sermon...

Don't go thinking **MASS** and **WEIGHT** are the same thing — mass is the <u>amount of matter</u> in something (measured in kg), weight is the <u>force</u> (measured in Newtons) on it from the pull of gravity. It's yet another formula you can put into a formula triangle, so it's nice 'n' easy.

See p21 (Higher) or p24 (Foundation) of our Revision Guide

Mass and Weight

Exam questions about mass and weight are often in bits of questions about something else. But not always.

Q1 A parachutist has a mass of 70 kg. His parachute has a mass of 10 kg.

a) What is their combined weight?

Watch out: don't think all you have to do is add up 70 and 10. It's <u>weight</u> you're after, not mass...

b) At the time this picture was taken, the force upwards due to air resistance was 670 N. What was the resultant force downwards?

Hmm — this is pretty tough. Think about using F=ma where F is the net force downwards (see p13).

c) What was the parachutist's acceleration at that point in time?

Q2 Victor and his dog weigh 1176 N together. Victor has a mass of 63 kg.

Watch out — you've got a mixture of kg and N.

a) What is the mass of Victor's dog?

b) Victor, his dog and his saxophone are standing on a box. Victor's saxophone has a mass of 2 kg and the box weighs 30 N. What is the total weight of them all?

c) Victor's dog jumps off the box. About half way to the ground, his acceleration is 8 m/s². What is the upward force on the dog, due to air resistance, at that point?

Eeeek — this is a nasty one. Remember: the acceleration is due to the NET force downwards — that's the weight <u>minus</u> air resistance.

Q3 Paddy O'Paddle and his boat have a mass of 125 kg together. The boat weighs 417 N.

a) What is the mass of the boat?

b) What is the combined weight of Paddy and his boat?

c) What is Paddy's weight?

d) As he goes over a waterfall in the boat, Paddy's acceleration is 6.5 m/s². What is the upward force on Paddy and his boat due to air resistance as they fall?

Damon Hill's rubbish at Physics — he only knows one formula...

Don't get fazed when you get 2 formulas in the same question. It's just as easy as doing them separately. You work out the answer to one formula, then bung that answer in the next formula. No clever tricks, no conspiracy theory — just do one bit, then do the other bit. Cheesy peas.

See p21 (Higher) or p24 (Foundation) of our Revision Guide

Speed and Velocity

$$\text{speed} = \frac{d}{t} \quad \text{Distance} \atop \text{Time}$$

Make sure your values for d and t are in the right units.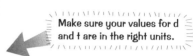

EG:
Find speed if d=40 m
and t=6 s

Speed = 40 ÷ 6 = 6.7 m/s

Give answers on this page to 1 d.p.

Q1 Work out the speed of a car travelling on a straight track for:

a) 100 m in 10 s   d) 1000 m in 200 s   g) 320 m in 16 s

b) 300 m in 20 s   e) 1500 m in 180 s   h) 50 m in 4 s

c) 700 m in 35 s   f) 450 m in 22 s   i) 500 m in 60 s

Q2 How far does a lorry move if it's travelling at:

Watch out for tricky units.

a) 10 m/s for 30 s   d) 15 m/s for 28 s   g) 15 m/s for 20 mins

b) 20 m/s for 20 s   e) 12 m/s for 180 s   h) 100 km/h for 300 s

c) 2 m/s for 100 s   f) 5 m/s for 70 s   i) 180 km/h for 20 mins

Q3 How long does it take a car to travel:

a) 10 m at 20 m/s   d) 180 m at 6 m/s   g) 50 km at 100 km/h

b) 50 m at 10 m/s   e) 40 m at 12 m/s   h) 55.5 km at 80 km/h

c) 200 m at 8 m/s   f) 1100 m at 14 m/s   i) 2 km at 16 m/s

Q4 What's the speed of:

a) A postman walking his route of 1 km in 900 s?

b) A snail crawling 10 cm in 60 s?

c) A cyclist on a track covering 200 m in 15 s?

d) Herbie the Beetle racing at 1 km in 1 minute?

e) A triple jumper bouncing 17 m in 8 s?

f) A boyracer driving 2 km in 75 s?

g) A giraffe strolling 120 m in 200 s?

h) A streaker running 100 m in 15 s?

i) A satellite travelling 4 km in 2 s?

Having tried everything else, the only option for pole position was go-faster stripes.

What's Damon Hill's favourite physics topic — radioactivity...

Working out speed gets you <u>easy marks</u> in the exam. It might be hidden among other things but it's a cast-iron <u>guarantee</u> that you'll get a question on it. You've got to learn that formula — by the time the exams come round, you'll be keeping the neighbours awake by shouting it in your sleep.

See p26 (Higher) or p30 (Foundation) of our Revision Guide

Speed and Velocity

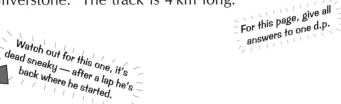

$$v = \frac{d}{t}$$

Velocity   Displacement / Time

For velocity, 'd' is the <u>displacement</u> rather than the distance.

EG:
Find velocity if d = 40 m and t = 6 s

Velocity = 40 ÷ 6 = 6.7 m/s

Q1 A bike racer is riding on his new bike at Silverstone. The track is 4 km long.

For this page, give all answers to one d.p.

a) What is his average speed in km/h if he does a lap in 2 mins 10 s?

b) What is his <u>velocity</u> after one lap? ⟵ *Watch out for this one, it's dead sneaky — after a lap he's back where he started.*

c) How long will it take to complete the lap while racing at 100 km/h?

d) The superbike racer completes his final lap in 1 min 20 s. Work out his average speed for the last lap in km/h.

Velocity has direction because it depends on <u>displacement</u> — the distance and direction from the <u>starting position</u>.

Q2 A jet has a top speed of 1500 km/h.

a) The pilot boasts that he can fly at 410 m/s. Is he telling the truth?

1 mile = 1.609 km

b) Darlington is 470 miles north-east of Farnborough. It takes 40 mins for the pilot to fly to Darlington in a straight line from Farnborough. Work out his velocity in km/h.

c) After re-fuelling, the pilot leaves Darlington and flies south at top speed for 535 km then due west back to Farnborough for 535 km at 1000 km/h. How long does his return journey take?

d) Was the journey to Farnborough faster than the journey to Darlington?

Q3 A team of rowers are training on the Thames. The river's flowing in an easterly direction.

a) The captain gets there early and warms up. It takes him 30 s to row 100 m in the direction of water flow. What is his velocity in m/s?

b) The team of eight row 500 m in 180 s. If they keep going at the same speed, how long will it take them to row a full 2 km?

c) The world record for an 8-man team is 2 km in 6 minutes. How long would it take the record-holders to row 500 m at the same speed? How does this compare to the speed of the team on the Thames?

d) The captain decides to show the team how it's done. He rows 2 km in 7 mins. What's his speed in m/s?

e) The captain realises he's gone a bit too far so he hitches a lift back on a passing speedboat. Its speedo says 55 km/h. How long does it take for him to get back to the team?

Faster than a velociting bullet...

Speed's pretty straightforward, but don't forget that velocity must have a <u>direction</u>. If a car's been driven East at a <u>speed</u> of 10 m/s, its <u>velocity</u> was 10 m/s E or 10 m/s 090°. You'll be throwing marks away if you mix up speed and velocity. Grit your teeth and practise 'til it hurts.

See p26 (Higher) or p30 (Foundation) of our Revision Guide

Acceleration

$$a = \frac{(v-u)}{t}$$

Acceleration = Change in velocity / Time taken

EG:
Find a if u=2 m/s,
v=4 m/s and t=1s

$$a = 2 \div 1 = 2 \, m/s^2$$

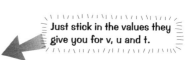
Just stick in the values they give you for v, u and t.

'u' is the initial velocity, and 'v' is the final velocity.

Q1 Find the acceleration if the velocity changes from:

Acceleration is the change in metres per second per second. So stick another 's' in the units to get m/s².

a) 2 m/s to 4 m/s in 4 s

b) 5 m/s to 10 m/s in 2 s

c) 100 m/s to 120 m/s in 5 s

d) 86 m/s to 94 m/s in 4 s

e) 21 m/s to 35 m/s in 18 s

f) 2 m/s to 36 m/s in 4 s

g) 0 m/s to 12 m/s in 9 s

h) 40 m/s to 42 m/s in 8 s

i) 11 m/s to 67 m/s in 3 s

j) 124 m/s to 345 m/s in 12 s

Answers on this page to 1 d.p. again.

So this is what they mean by 0 to 60 in 4 seconds...

Q2 How long does it take a car to change from:

a) 6 m/s to 10 m/s at 2 m/s²

b) 30 m/s to 60 m/s at 5 m/s²

c) 2 m/s to 74 m/s at 8 m/s²

d) 18 m/s to 50 m/s at 5 m/s²

e) 12 m/s to 38 m/s at 6 m/s²

f) 1.5 m/s to 7 m/s at 1.1 m/s²

g) 35 m/s to 42 m/s at 7.2 m/s²

h) 12.4 m/s to 18.6 m/s at 4 m/s²

i) 0 km/h to 160 km/h at 20 m/s²

j) 152 km/h to 168 km/h at 30 m/s²

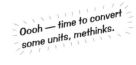
Oooh — time to convert some units, methinks.

Q3 What's the acceleration of:

0 m/s is just another way of saying 'standing still'.

a) A moonwalking astronaut going from 1 m/s to 3 m/s in 40 s?

b) A hare going from sitting still to hopping at 2 m/s in 0.5 s?

c) A cyclist moving off from stationary to 15 m/s in 5 mins?

d) A jet flying at 52 m/s increasing its velocity to 125 m/s in 12 s?

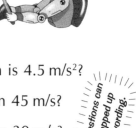
There must be a better way to decelerate....

e) How long does it take a truck to go from 5 m/s to 28 m/s if its acceleration is 4.5 m/s²?

f) If a juggernaut decelerates at 9 m/s², how long will it take him to stop from 45 m/s?

g) A firework accelerates at 5 m/s². How long does it take to go from 2 m/s to 30 m/s?

h) A car does an emergency stop from 120 km/h in 3 s. What was its deceleration?

Easy questions can come wrapped up in tricky wording.

i) (For bonus marks...) What was the car's average velocity and what was the stopping distance?

Accelerate your learning — throw your teacher off a cliff...

Anyone thinking that acceleration and velocity are the same thing needs whacking over the head with a weighty Physics textbook. **Velocity** means <u>how fast</u>, acceleration means how quickly the velocity is <u>changing</u>. Think about cars — foot on accelerator makes you <u>change speed</u>.

See p26 (Higher) or p30 (Foundation) of our Revision Guide

Velocity and Acceleration

This page has some whopping great questions on it. Take a deep breath and give 'em your best shot. Give all answers to one decimal place.

Q1 A team of pilots are testing a prototype of a new kind of rocket.

Don't let all these units give you brainache. These are easy marks in the exam.

a) It's 20 000 kilometres from Manchester to Sydney, Australia. The rocket does the journey in 4 hours. What was the average speed for the trip in m/s?

b) If the rocket could go straight through the centre of the Earth, the distance is only 12 740 km. If the rocket travelled at the same speed, how long would it take to get to Sydney?

c) From lift-off, the team can get the rocket up to 2 km/s in 14 seconds. What's the acceleration of the rocket in m/s²?

Q2 It's 70 miles by road from Birmingham to Oxford. The journey usually takes me 1 hour and 10 minutes on the motorway.

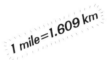

1 mile=1.609 km

a) How far is the journey in kilometres?

b) What's my average speed during the journey in mph and km/h?

c) I could get to Oxford in 45 minutes if I went faster. How fast would I have to go and would this be legal? (The motorway speed limit is 70 mph.)

d) Yesterday I overtook a caravan that was doing 80 km/h. The velocity of my car increased from 80 km/h to 110 km/h in 4 seconds. What was my acceleration, in m/s²?

Q3 Sound travels at a rather stately 330 m/s in air.

Light travels around 1000 times faster than sound, so assume the lightning is seen the instant it strikes.

a) I looked at my watch the moment I saw a flash of lightning and heard the thunder 12 seconds later. To the nearest kilometre, how far away did the lightning strike?

b) A girl and boy are standing under a tree. The boy starts running, accelerating at 0.2 m/s². What speed is he running at when he reaches the middle of the field 18 seconds later?

c) The middle of the field is 32.4 m away. What was the boy's average speed?

d) If the girl yells at the boy from under the tree, how long will it take her voice to reach him?

e) The next flash of lightning lights up the sky. It takes 18 s this time before I hear the rumble of thunder. How far away is it now? Is is getting closer or further away?

Velocity and Acceleration — that famous comedy duo...

Physics — it's all so useful. Handy for all kinds of situations. Driving, athletics, thunderstorms... oh and let's not forget the EXAMS. Those formulas need to be stuffed into your overflowing grey cells, ready to leap onto the paper and make the examiner drop his hobnob in his tea with delight.

See p11 (Higher) or p13 (Foundation) of our Revision Guide

Waves

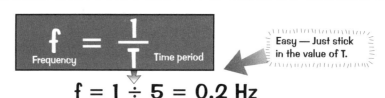

$$f = \frac{1}{T}$$

Frequency   Time period

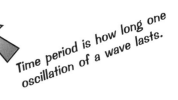

Easy — Just stick in the value of T.

EG:
Find f if T=5 s

$$f = 1 \div 5 = 0.2 \text{ Hz}$$

Q1 Work out the wave frequency for waves with these time periods:

a) 10 s   c) 4 s   e) 20 s   g) 0.2 s

b) 5 s   d) 2 s   f) 1 s   h) 0.01 s

Time period is how long one oscillation of a wave lasts.

Q2 Find the time period for these waves with the following frequencies:

a) 20 Hz   c) 0.1 Hz   e) 250 Hz   g) 0.002 Hz

b) 2 Hz   d) 1000 Hz   f) 4 Hz   h) 125 Hz

You'll have to re-arrange that formula.

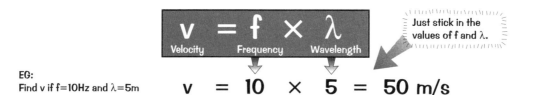

$$v = f \times \lambda$$

Velocity   Frequency   Wavelength

Just stick in the values of f and λ.

EG:
Find v if f=10Hz and λ=5m

$$v = 10 \times 5 = 50 \text{ m/s}$$

Q3 These waves all have a wavelength of 12m. Calculate their velocity if they have the following frequencies.

a) 2 Hz   d) 20 Hz   g) 1000 Hz

b) 5 Hz   e) 1 Hz   h) 8 Hz

c) 10 Hz   f) 0.5 Hz   i) 1.2 Hz

Q4 These waves have a frequency of 10 Hz. Find the wavelength if they have these velocities:

a) 3 m/s   d) 0.3 m/s   g) 50 m/s

b) 40 m/s   e) 2500 m/s   h) 20 m/s

c) 100 m/s   f) 0.2 m/s   i) 100 cm/s

Q5 Find the velocity of waves with these time periods and wavelengths:

a) time period: 10 s.   b) time period: 5 s.   c) time period: 1 min.

   wavelength: 20 m.   wavelength: 12 m   wavelength: 15 m.

You'll need to use both equations for this one.

Everybody's gone surfing — surfing VFλ...

This stuff's hideously simple — It's just two more triangle formulas. Hertz are just '<u>waves per second</u>', so don't get in a flap about them. Don't get in a muddle with your units either — just convert everything to <u>metres</u>, <u>seconds</u> and <u>hertz</u>. Then it'll be a piece of cake.

See p35 (Higher) or p40 (Foundation) of our Revision Guide

Waves

Here are some longer questions but don't panic — they're pretty much the same thing.
Just shove the numbers in the <u>right</u> places in the <u>right</u> formulas.

Q1   Jack threw his annoying little sister Jill in the garden pond.
     Jill made a large splash and waves rippled across the pond.

   a) If each wave has a time period of 2 s, what is their frequency?

   b) If the same waves travel across the pond at a speed of 5 m/s, what is their wavelength?

   c) Jack wants to see what
     happens if he throws Jill
     into different ponds.
     Finish off his results
     table.

Pond	Frequency Hz	Wavelength m	Velocity m/s
A	20	0.3	
B	2		7
C	5	1.2	
D		0.4	5

   d) On his last throw Jack got so excited he forgot to record the frequency.
     Luckily he noticed that Jill's shoe had fallen off and bobbed up and
     down 20 times in 10 seconds. Which pond had he thrown her in?

Q2   In a revenge attack Jill plays her stereo at top volume
     when Jack is trying to do his physics homework.

Watch your units — 1 kHz is 1000 Hz.

   a) The sound waves travel through the wall to Jack's room. The waves have
     a frequency of 6 kHz and wavelength of 15 cm. What is their velocity?

   b) Jack covers his head with a pillow. Through the pillow the sound wave has a
     frequency of 6 kHz and a velocity of 400 m/s. What is its wavelength in cm?

   c) Jack gives up studying and puts on his radio. He listens to his favourite Radio 4
     programme on the origins of the universe. Radio 4 transmits radio waves with a
     wavelength of 1.5 km. They travel at the speed of light. What is their frequency?

Use 3×10^8 m/s as an approximation of the speed of light.

Q3   With this data you can work out and use a more accurate
     figure for the speed of light. Give answers to 4 s.f.

   a) Blue light has a frequency of 7×10^{14}. It has a
     wavelength of 4.287×10^{-7}. What is its velocity?

   b) Red light has a wavelength of 7.49×10^{-7}.
     It travels with the same velocity as blue
     light. What is its frequency?

Go dancing with Jonathan Ross — go to a wave...

A tricky thing about waves is the <u>range of sizes</u> they come in. <u>Wavelengths</u> can vary from cm to km.
<u>Velocity</u> can be anything from a fraction of a metre per second to the <u>speed of light</u>. It's difficult
when some of your answers look ridiculous, but don't be put off. I'm sure you'll get it right...

See p35 (Higher) or p40 (Foundation) of our Revision Guide

Moments

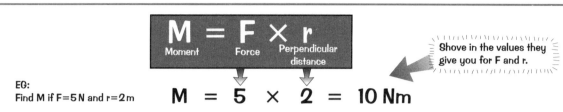

$$M = F \times r$$

Moment   Force   Perpendicular distance

Shove in the values they give you for F and r.

EG:
Find M if F=5N and r=2m

$$M = 5 \times 2 = 10 \text{ Nm}$$

Q1 For each of the pictures, work out the moment and say whether it's clockwise or anticlockwise.

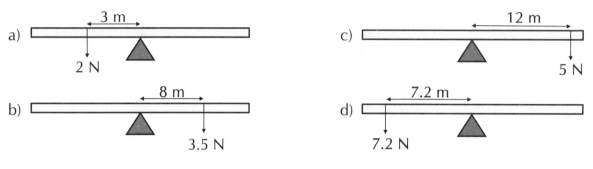

a)   3 m   2 N

b)   8 m   3.5 N

c)   12 m   5 N

d)   7.2 m   7.2 N

Q2 Find the total clockwise and anticlockwise moments for these seesaws. Which side will tip down — the LEFT or the RIGHT?

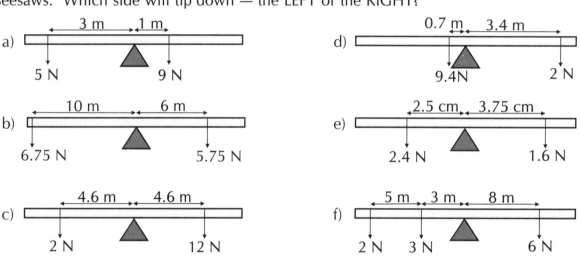

a)   3 m   1 m   5 N   9 N

b)   10 m   6 m   6.75 N   5.75 N

c)   4.6 m   4.6 m   2 N   12 N

d)   0.7 m   3.4 m   9.4N   2 N

e)   2.5 cm   3.75 cm   2.4 N   1.6 N

f)   5 m   3 m   8 m   2 N   3 N   6 N

Q3 A 1 kg frog is sitting on a seesaw.

Use g=10N/kg

a) What is the <u>force</u> on the seesaw, 2 m right of the pivot, due to the frog's mass?

b) What is the moment about the pivot due to this mass? Is this clockwise or anticlockwise?

c) A cat has a mass of 2 kg. What happens if he sits on the other side of the seesaw, 2 m from the pivot?

d) Where does the cat need to sit so that the seesaw is balanced?

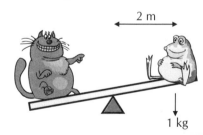

2 m

1 kg

Momentous...

If there's more than one force on one side of the pivot then just add the moments together one by one. If you get muddled by clockwise and anticlockwise, wear an analogue watch in the exam. It's all too easy to get your directions in a pickle, but keep a cool head and it'll be fine.

See p21 (Higher) or p35 (Foundation) of our Revision Guide

Moments

Simple, this moment lark. If you haven't been given a diagram, sketch one out.
It doesn't take long and it'll make things a lot easier.

Q1   A rabbit is using a fishing line to hook a carrot out of the water.

a) Calculate the moment of the 65 N force about the pivot.

b) The pull exerted by the rabbit is balanced by the pull in
the fishing line. Work out the tension in the fishing line.

c) The fishing line will break if the tension becomes
more than 60 N. If the pull is in the same direction as
before, what's the maximum force the rabbit can use?

Pull 65 N   **Tension**
                  2 m
Pivot   **0.5 m**

Q2   A 5 m long plank is pivoted at <u>one end</u>. The plank
is held up at the other end so that it is horizontal.

Aaaargh...no diagram. Don't panic, draw your own.

a) If a man weighing 500 N stands on the plank, 3 m from the pivot,
what upward force is needed to keep the plank horizontal?

b) What force is needed to keep the plank horizontal
if the man stands 4 m from the pivot?

c) If the man puts on his thick coat, which weighs 60 N, and
stands 2 m from the pivot, how much force will the person
holding the end of the plank need to keep the plank level?

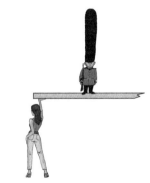

d) The plank-holder can push with a maximum force of 550 N
upwards. Can she keep the plank level if the man stands 3 m
from the pivot wearing the coat and a 200 N hat?

Q3   There are three handles on this door. The hinge
needs a moment of 20 Nm to open the door.

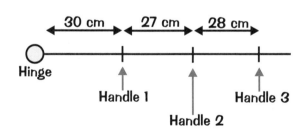

a) If handle 1 is pushed with a force of 10 N,
nothing happens. Why won't the door open?

b) What (to 1d.p) is the smallest pushing force
needed to open the door with handle 2?

c) What's the minimum force (to 1 d.p.) needed to open the door with handle 3?

d) Why are door handles usually on the opposite side to the hinges?

<u>Moment = Torque = Turning Force...</u>   <u>= no fun but you've got to learn it</u>

Moment is a pretty silly name. Think of it as a <u>turning force</u> — that'll help you picture what the
force is doing. If the question doesn't give you a diagram, you'll have to draw one for yourself.
They <u>don't</u> tell you this of course, oh no. You <u>really</u> need to do it though, it makes it <u>much easier</u>.

See p21 (Higher) or p35 (Foundation) of our Revision Guide

Hooke's Law

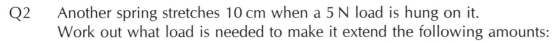

extension = F × k
Force   Constant

EG:
Find E if F=10 N and k=3

E = 10 × 3 = 30 cm

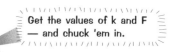

Get the values of k and F — and chuck 'em in.

Q1 A spring has k = 0.75. Work out how far it'll stretch with these loads:

Give answers to 3 s.f.

a) 8 N	d) 3 N	g) 14 N
b) 12 N	e) 9 N	h) 5.5 N
c) 1 N	f) 13 N	i) 7.5 N

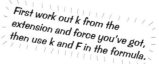

Q2 Another spring stretches 10 cm when a 5 N load is hung on it.
Work out what load is needed to make it extend the following amounts:

a) 20 cm	d) 5 cm	g) 17 cm
b) 2 cm	e) 15 cm	h) 9.5 cm
c) 8 cm	f) 13 cm	i) 1.5 cm

First work out k from the extension and force you've got, then use k and F in the formula.

Q3 Yet another went from 10 cm to 15 cm long with a 2 N load on it.
Work out the <u>total length</u> of the spring with these loads:

a) 4 N	d) 3 N	g) 6.5 N
b) 6 N	e) 0.5 N	h) 3.5 N
c) 1 N	f) 7 N	i) 9 N

Remember that the formula uses the <u>extension</u>, not the <u>total length</u>.

Q4 One last spring is 20 cm long with nothing hanging from it. With a 400 g mass on the end, the spring is 27 cm long. Work out what masses would be needed to make the spring these lengths:

Give masses in grams, to the nearest whole number.

a) 34 cm	d) 20 cm	g) 42.5 cm
b) 41 cm	e) 21.5 cm	h) 40.3 cm
c) 38 cm	f) 35.5 cm	i) 26.7 cm

Use g=10 N/kg.

Q5 The spring is swapped for an elastic band that extends from 10 cm to 25 cm long when a 400 g mass is hung on the end. Work out the total length with these masses on the end:

a) 150 g	d) 420 g	g) 50 g
b) 275 g	e) 660 g	h) 510 g
c) 715 g	f) 340 g	i) 825 g

It's an elastic band, not a spring, but you do the question in exactly the same way.

I don't get on with my past girlfriends — too much ex-tension...

Okay. The main thing here is that Hooke's Law can tell you how much things will stretch. Just remember that each spring has its own value for the constant 'k'. Just multiply that by F and that's your extension. Once you got the hang of that, there's nothing to it. Lovely-jubbly.

See p30 (Higher) or p34 (Foundation) of our Revision Guide

Hooke's Law

Don't be put off by all the words — these questions may look harder, but they're just like the ones on the last page. Just find the values for each of the parts of the formula and shove them in. And you get to draw a graph, too. More fun than you could possibly imagine.

Q1 Here are some results from investigating the extension of a steel spring when different weights are hung from it.

Load (N)	Extension (cm)
0	0
1	12
2	24
3	36
4	48
5	54
6	57

a) Using the results table, plot a graph of extension (in cm) against load (in Newtons).

b) On the graph you've drawn, mark the elastic limit with a cross. What happens to the spring once it's reached the elastic limit?

You can work out k from the formula — but the easy way is that it's the slope of the graph.

c) What is the value of the constant 'k' for the spring?

d) The spring was 22 cm long at the start of the experiment. What load, to 3 s.f, could be added to make it 53 cm long?

e) How long would the spring be with a load of 3.4 N applied to it?

f) How much would the spring extend if a 250 g mass were hung on the end?

Q2 A physics teacher is using a troop of circus monkeys to demonstrate Hooke's Law for a large spring. Each monkey has a mass of 900 g.

Use g=10 N/kg.

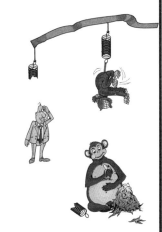

a) With one monkey on the spring, the total length is 49 cm. With three monkeys, its total length is 67 cm. How long will the spring be when two monkeys are hung from it?

b) What's the value of the constant 'k' for the spring?

c) How long will the spring be with no monkeys on it?

d) The elastic limit of the spring is reached when a force of 50 N is applied to it. How long will the spring be when it reaches its elastic limit?

Q3 Last week the teacher took his entire physics class (and the monkeys) to the Moon to do the same experiment. On the Moon g = 1.6 N/kg.

a) How long will the spring be with one monkey hanging on it, to the nearest tenth of a centimetre?

b) How many monkeys would be needed to get an extension of at least 10 cm?

c) How many monkeys could be hung on the spring before it reaches its elastic limit?

Aaah, Hooke's law — the first sign of spring...

All this is pretty standard stuff. All it means when there's a constant in the formula is that one thing is <u>proportional</u> to the other — in this case, if you stretch something with a steadily increasing force, then the length will increase steadily too. Learn the formula and <u>don't forget your units.</u>

See p30 (Higher) or p34 (Foundation) of our Revision Guide

Pressure = Force ÷ Area

$$P = \frac{F}{A}$$

Pressure = Force / Area

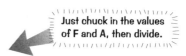

Just chuck in the values of F and A, then divide.

EG:
Find P if F=500 N and A=10 m²

$$P = 500 \div 10 = 50 \, Pa$$

Q1 Snowshoes are made with different sizes of sole. To the nearest whole number, work out the pressure someone weighing 350 N would exert on the snow if wearing soles with the following total areas:

a) 0.1 m²   d) 0.15 m²   g) 0.19 m²

b) 0.3 m²   e) 0.24 m²   h) 0.04 m²

c) 0.25 m²   f) 0.07 m²   i) 0.12 m²

Q2 What area would you need to spread a force of 13 N over to get the following pressures?

a) 13 Pa   d) 130 Pa   g) 2 Pa

b) 5 Pa   e) 52 Pa   h) 12.5 Pa

c) 17 Pa   f) 82 Pa   i) 27.5 Pa

0.3 m

Q3 A skater has a mass of 70 kg. Her super-fast racing skates have blades that are 30 cm long. Work out the pressure on the ice of a blade with each of the following thicknesses:

a) 2 mm   d) 5 mm   g) 11 mm

b) 1 cm   e) 0.9 cm   h) 4.3 mm

c) 3.5 mm   f) 0.75 cm   i) 0.56 cm

You can use N/cm² instead of Pascals, but they're not the same thing.

Q4 A suitcase is 75 cm long and 50 cm deep. What pressure will it exert on the ground (in Pa) if it weighs these amounts:

Give all answers to 3 s.f.

a) 26 kg   d) 16.5 kg   g) 8.25 kg

b) 12 kg   e) 19.5 kg   h) 13.75 kg

c) 9 kg   f) 4.5 kg   i) 22.25 kg

Q5 A slalom skier has a mass of 80 kg. He uses skis that are 10 cm wide. Work out the pressure (in Pa) these different lengths of skis exert on the ground when the skier is wearing them.

Remember that people usually have two feet.

a) 90 cm   d) 180 cm   g) 1.9 m

b) 1.1 m   e) 220 cm   h) 200 cm

c) 2.3 m   f) 1.5 m   i) 1.75 m

Like you don't have enough pressure already...

It's understanding the difference between <u>force</u> and <u>pressure</u> that might give you a wee bit of bother here. An easy-peasy way of describing pressure is just <u>force per unit area</u>. A large force on a small area means high pressure, and a small force on a large area means low pressure. Easy.

See p32 (Higher) or p36 (Foundation) of our Revision Guide

Pressure and Hydraulics

Pressure is a big topic for the exam — especially questions like this first one.
There are questions like this in the exam all the time.

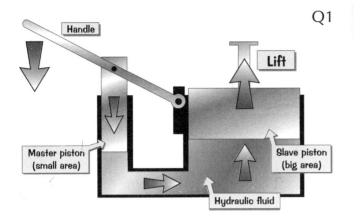

Handle

Lift

Master piston
(small area)

Slave piston
(big area)

Hydraulic fluid

Q1 This hydraulic jack has a master piston of area 5 cm² and a slave piston of area 60 cm².

a) If a force of 600 N is applied to the master piston, how much pressure will be transferred to the hydraulic fluid?

b) What will be the force produced at the slave piston?

c) How many times has the original force been multiplied?

Q2 For the same hydraulic jack, work out the force produced at the slave piston if these forces are applied at the master piston.

a) 700 N   d) 175 N   g) 853 N

b) 100 N   e) 325 N   h) 47 N

c) 250 N   f) 405 N   i) 634 N

1000 kg

Q3 Another hydraulic system has a master piston with a radius of 3.7 cm and a slave piston of radius 9.2 cm.

a) If a force of 400 N is applied to the master piston, how much pressure will be created in the system, to one d.p?

Use π=3.14

b) What will be the force produced at the slave piston, to the nearest whole number?

c) How many times, to 1 d.p, has the original force been multiplied?

d) How many baby gorillas, each with a mass of 45 kg, could be lifted by the slave piston?

Q4 For these pairs of pistons, work out the force produced at the slave piston with a force of 150 N applied at the master piston. Give answers to the nearest whole number.

a) master: 6 cm²
   slave: 45 cm²

b) master: 8.5 cm²
   slave: 92 cm²

c) master: 5 cm²
   slave: 82 cm²

d) master: 10 cm²
   slave: 26 cm²

e) master: 7.25 cm²
   slave: 50 cm²

f) master: 4.3 cm²
   slave: 27.4 cm²

g) master: 9.2 cm²
   slave: 43 cm²

h) master: 8.5 cm²
   slave: 68 cm²

My GT550's got hydraulic brakes — boring but true...

That old pressure formula should be second nature by now. The tricky bit is how the formula is applied <u>twice</u> to explain how hydraulic systems can turn a <u>small</u> force into a <u>big</u> one. Hard to get your head round, but keep slaving — you'll soon realise it's <u>much</u> easier than it looks.

See p32 (Higher) or p37 (Foundation) of our Revision Guide

Pressure = Force ÷ Area

The key to these is extracting the information from all these words. Make sure you work out what each letter is and you get the units right — then it's just that old pressure equation again.

Q1   A group of six bored friends have been drawing around the soles of their left shoes and measuring their area.

Use g=10 N/kg.

a) Work out how much each person weighs in Newtons.

b) To 2 d.p, work out how much pressure each person exerts on the ground while standing on <u>both</u> feet.

c) What would happen to the pressure if they all lifted one foot off the ground?

d) Who exerts the most pressure?

e) What could Chris, Iain and Steve change about their footwear to increase the pressure their two feet exert on the ground?

Name	Area of Left Sole	Mass
Chris	300 cm²	65 kg
Simah	160 cm²	50 kg
Steve	320 cm²	75 kg
Pam	220 cm²	60 kg
Sheetal	200 cm²	55 kg
Iain	310 cm²	70 kg

Q2   An iron has a mass of 1.4 kg and an area of 0.025 m².

a) Work out the pressure on the clothes if no extra force is put on the iron.

b) What will be the pressure on the clothes if an extra force of 20 N is put on the iron?

c) What extra downward force must be applied to the iron to create a pressure of 2000 Pa?

d) A particularly tricky crease in a silk tie needs a pressure of 2200 Pa to iron it out. If an extra downward force of 40 N is applied, will this be enough to press the crease out?

Q3   Boris, Ivan and Natasha are circus performers. Boris has a mass of 70 kg, Ivan is 65 kg and Natasha is 45 kg. Give answers in N/cm², to 3 s.f.

a) The tip of Natasha's ballet shoe forms a circle of radius 1 cm. What pressure does Natasha exert on the ground while balancing on one toe?

Use π=3.14.

b) The palms of Ivan's hands are 9 cm across. Work out how much pressure he exerts on his trapeze, which is 3 cm thick.

The tricky bit here is to work out the area of his hand <u>on the trapeze</u>.

c) Boris is standing on the back of a baby elephant. The elephant has a mass of 600 kg. If each of the elephant's feet have a 15 cm radius, what pressure do Boris and the elephant exert on the ground?

d) Natasha's feet are 20 cm long. What pressure does she exert on the 1 cm thick high wire when balancing on one foot?

Although pressure is usually measured in Pascals (N/m²), no-one minds if you give your answer in N/cm². It's much easier when working with small areas like human feet and clothes irons. Just make sure the units are the same on both sides of the equation, or it'll all go pear-shaped.

See p32 (Higher) or p36 (Foundation) of our Revision Guide

Work Done = Force × Distance

$$Wd = F \times d$$
Work done   Force   Distance

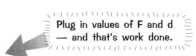
Plug in values of F and d
— and that's work done.

EG:
Find Wd if F=20 N and d=5 m

$$Wd = 20 \times 5 = 100 \text{ J}$$

Q1   Find the work done having pushed a shopping trolley with a force of 50 N over the following distances:

Remember to change all measurements to metres before you use the formula.

a) 100 m   d) 430 m   g) 177 m

b) 50 cm   e) 2 km   h) 1355 m

c) 25 m   f) 73 m   i) 986.5 m

Q2   A weightlifter lifts weights 50 cm. Find the work done for each of the following:

a) 10 kg   d) 20 kg   g) 35 kg

b) 60 kg   e) 120 kg   h) 105 kg

c) 55 kg   f) 75 kg   i) 95 kg

Q3   Bricks weighing 1.5 kg are lifted on a platform weighing 3 kg. To the nearest joule, find the work done if the following number of bricks (on the platform) are lifted 5 m:

a) 50   d) 22   g) 19

b) 35   e) 44   h) 53

c) 65   f) 67   i) 71

Q4   Find the work done in the following situations:

a) A stubborn dog being pulled over 5 m of tarmac with a force of 300 N.

b) A car being pushed 1 km with a force of 1600 N.

c) A pram being pushed 2 km with a force of 50 N.

d) A coffee cup of 500 g being raised 40 cm.

e) A rollerblader being pulled 100 m with a force of 100 N.

f) A water-skier being pulled across a harbour 400 m wide with a force of 450 N.

g) A window cleaner of mass 70 kg climbing a ladder 7 m high.

h) A mobile home with a mass of 4000 kg being raised 1 m.

4's 4 U 2 do...

Work done is the same thing as energy transferred, and you can't transfer energy without moving something. Remember that and you're halfway there. What matters is how far you've moved whatever it is, and how much force it took. Work done=Force×distance. Remember it.

See p64 (Higher) or p63 (Foundation) of our Revision Guide

Work Done = Force × Distance

You've already done some questions with this formula. This page just shows how they might come up in the real world (or an exam). Don't just sit there — get some work done.

Q1   A car has broken down on the isolated, winding Cumbrian roads.
There's a garage 2000 metres away, along a flat coastal route.

a) It needs a minimum force of 900 N to push the car along a flat road.
What is the minimum energy the driver needs to get the car to the garage?

b) There's another garage 1400 metres away, but it's higher
up in the fells along a steep road. The pushing force here
would have to be 1700 N. Calculate the total work
done if the driver chooses this garage instead.

c) The driver decides he doesn't want to push the car uphill
so he chooses the garage on the flat road. Halfway there he
notices the road's been resurfaced. It now only takes 700 N to push the car.
What is the total energy consumption by the time he gets to the garage?

*OK — this is tougher.
Work it out for the 1st half
and 2nd half separately,
then add them together.*

Q2   The weightlifter's back in the gym. He's working on loads of different machines this time.

a) The weightlifter lifts 50 kg 40 times. Each time he lifts the
load 30 cm. Calculate the work done.

Use g=10 N/kg.

b) This time he does 20 lifts, then bumps the load up to 80 kg and
does 10 more. How much work is done this time?

c) The weightlifter moves on to another machine which raises the load
65 cm. How much energy does he use doing 15 lifts of 80 kg?

d) How many lifts of 60 kg (raising the load 65 cm) would use
10 530 J of energy?

Q3   Five secretaries are participating in an annual 'pull the boss' competition.

a) What is the work done by the secretaries together if
they move the boss 150 m with a force of 240 N?

b) What is the work done by the secretaries together if
they move the boss 1600 m with a force of 130 N?

c) How far did they move the boss if they
used 6120 J and used a force of 200 N?

*Don't forget to divide by the
number of people at the end...*

d) What was the work done by each of the secretaries if all
five of them worked equally, and together they pulled the
boss 675 m with a force of 150 N?

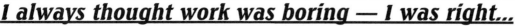

I always thought work was boring — I was right...

I always get my brain in a right old twist with this one — it's weird thinking that a man holding a piano above his head isn't doing any work because he's not taking it anywhere. But no-one's saying you have to understand it. You've only got to learn it. Thank goodness for that.

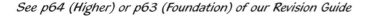

See p64 (Higher) or p63 (Foundation) of our Revision Guide

Power = Work ÷ Time

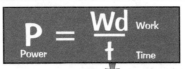

$$P = \frac{Wd}{t}$$ Power, Work, Time

Just shove in the values for Wd and t.

EG:
Find P if Wd=60 J and t=10 s

$$P = 60 \div 10 = 6\ W$$

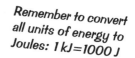
Remember to convert all units of energy to Joules: 1 kJ=1000 J

Q1 Work out the power of these electric fires, to the nearest watt, if they produce 1000 kJ in these amounts of time:

a) 200 seconds   d) 9 mins, 30 secs   g) 7 mins, 15 secs

b) 8 minutes   e) 6 mins, 30 secs   h) 8 mins, 43 secs

c) 10 minutes   f) 430 seconds   i) 5 mins, 29 secs

Q2 Work out the power of these toasters, to the nearest watt, if they produce these amounts of heat energy in 3 minutes:

a) 200 kJ   d) 150 kJ   g) 316 kJ

b) 400 kJ   e) 175 kJ   h) 257 kJ

c) 350 kJ   f) 225 kJ   i) 399 kJ

Time values should be converted to seconds.

Q3 A weightlifter's lifting bricks at a building site. He's doing a set of 10 lifts, raising a load of 50 kg by 40 cm. Work out his power, to 3 s.f, if he does the ten lifts in these times:

a) 2 minutes   d) 30 seconds   g) 27 seconds

b) 40 seconds   e) 95 seconds   h) 53 seconds

c) 1 minute   f) 115 seconds   i) 79 seconds

Watch out for the units, and remember that g=10 N/kg

Q4 An electric kettle is rated at 2400 watts. Work out how long it would take, to the nearest second, to supply the water with these amounts of energy:

a) 500 kJ   d) 850 kJ   g) 1313 kJ

b) 100 kJ   e) 955 kJ   h) 777 kJ

c) 350 kJ   f) 1145 kJ   i) 491 kJ

Q5 These wattages are written on the labels of a selection of hairdriers. How much heat energy (in kJ) will each one produce every minute?

a) 1 kW   d) 800 W   g) 1825 W

b) 1200 W   e) 950 W   h) 1075 W

c) 1600 W   f) 1450 W   i) 1375 W

Work divided by time to the people...

Power is a wee bit tricky to get your head round. Don't confuse it with force or energy. Powerful things can transfer a lot of energy in a short space of time. Luckily the formula's easy as pie so all you have to do is remember it and use it, and <u>don't mix up your units</u>.

See p64 (Higher) or p63 (Foundation) of our Revision Guide

Power = Work ÷ Time

More questions on power. They look wordier, and they are, but once you've found a
number for each of the letters in the formula, they're just like the ones on the page before.

Q1   A broken-down car is being pushed to a garage.

Give power to the nearest watt.

a) Work out the driver's power output if he takes 1 hour and
    45 minutes to push his car 2 km with a force of 900 N.

b) Work out the total power output if the driver has to stop for a 30 minute kip halfway there.

c) The driver's maximum power output is 500 W. How long would it
    take him to push the car to the garage at maximum output?

d) If the driver decides to take the uphill route, it would take a force of 1700 N to cover
    1400 m in 3 hours. Work out his power output, to the nearest whole number.

e) What percentage of his maximum power output is this?

Q2   The weightlifter's still lifting weights. The pulley he's working with lifts the load 50 cm each time.

a) The weightlifter spends 3 minutes doing 60 lifts of 45 kg. Work out his power output.

b) Work out the weightlifter's total power output if he
    does 3 sets of 10 lifts with 70 kg in 5 minutes.

Use g=10 N/kg.

c) Over the next 10 minutes, he does 50 lifts of 40 kg, 3 sets of
    10 lifts with 75 kg and 2 sets of 15 lifts with 60 kg. Work out
    his total power output to the nearest whole number.

d) The weightlifter's maximum power output is 100 W.
    At maximum power, how many times can he lift 80 kg in 4 minutes?

Q3   A team of 8 rowers are training on the Thames.

a) The rowers warm up by rowing with a combined force of 1600 N. They row for 5 minutes
    and cover a distance of 700 m. Work out the power output of the rowing team.

b) At racing speed, the team row with a combined force of 4000 N. They cover a distance
    of 3 km in 11 minutes. What is the average power output of the individual rowers?

c) During the cool-down session, the rowers apply a force of 100 N each. The team covers
    a distance of 400 m in 5 minutes. Work out the power output of the whole team.

d) The most powerful rower on the team is capable of an output of 3000 W, using a force of
    4000 N. How long would it take the team to row 3 km, if all the rowers were as good as this?

So much work to do, so little work divided by power...

I know I go on about units a bit, but they're really important. Unless all your distances are in
metres, your times are in seconds and your masses are converted to weight in Newtons, you'll end
up with a pile of ridiculous answers. Take your time and think carefully — you know it makes sense.

See p64 (Higher) or p63 (Foundation) of our Revision Guide

Efficiency

EG:
Find the efficiency if
Wd =1000 J and
Energy input =1250 J

$$\text{Efficiency} = \frac{\text{Work done}}{\text{Energy input}}$$

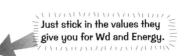
Just stick in the values they give you for Wd and Energy.

Efficiency = 1000 ÷ 1250 = 0.8 (80%)

Q1 Work out the efficiency of a machine if it does 1050 J of work with these energy inputs. Write your answer as a decimal, to 2 d.p.

a) 2000 J d) 3240 J g) 2001 J
b) 1500 J e) 10 500 J h) 1977 J
c) 4000 J f) 5250 J i) 1234 J

Efficiency has no units because it's joules divided by joules.

Q2 A machine gets 3500 J of electrical energy. Work out what its efficiency would be as a percentage, to the nearest 1%, if it did these amounts of work:

If you get an answer bigger than 100%, you know you're in trouble.

a) 3000 J d) 40 J g) 3105 J
b) 500 J e) 1400 J h) 2850 J
c) 3445 J f) 2500 J i) 759 J

Q3 A machine must do 5990 J of work. Calculate to the nearest joule the energy that must be supplied if the machine's efficiency is:

a) 0.5 c) 0.25 e) 70% g) 41%
b) 0.85 d) 0.1 f) 35% h) 90%

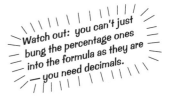
Watch out: you can't just bung the percentage ones into the formula as they are — you need decimals.

Q4 A pulling machine is 6% efficient. How much work can be done for each of these energy inputs:

a) 1000 J c) 50 000 J e) 8100 J
b) 2500 J d) 3400 J f) 6900 J

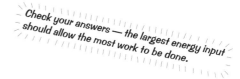
Check your answers — the largest energy input should allow the most work to be done.

Q5 A milk float uses 20 000 J to perform each of these tasks. Calculate how much work is done in each task, then calculate the milk float's efficiency to the nearest 1%.

a) driving uphill for 80 m, with a force of 200 N

b) racing downhill for 215 m, with a force of 80 N

c) driving over speed bumps for 90 m, with a force of 100 N

d) pushing a skip for 5 m, with a force of 3150 N

.... (3 marks)

Every few years, some boffin claims they've made a machine with more than 100% efficiency.
But if a more than 100% efficient machine exists, I'll eat my cat. So in the exam, <u>remember</u>
that and check all your answers are <u>less than 100% efficient</u>. Fluffy's depending on you.

See p63 (Higher) or p65 (Foundation) of our Revision Guide

Efficiency

$$\text{Efficiency} = \frac{\text{Useful energy out}}{\text{Total energy in}}$$

It's the same formula —this is just a different way of writing it.

EG:
Find the efficiency if
Useful output = 1000 J
and Total input = 1250 J

Efficiency = 1000 ÷ 1250 = 0.8 (80%)

The rest of the total energy is 'wasted', often as heat.

Q1 Work out the efficiency (as a percentage, to nearest 1%) of a speaker that is supplied with 2530 J, and gives out these amounts of sound energy:

a) 1000 J
d) 1600 J
g) 1490 J

b) 450 J
e) 250 J
h) 640 J

c) 900 J
f) 360 J
i) 1810 J

The sound energy is the useful energy here.

Q2 A guitar amp is 35% efficient. Work out the energy input, if the sound energy given out is:

a) 2000 J
c) 267 J
e) 7503 J

b) 4050 J
d) 8900 J
f) 10 890 J

Give the answer to the nearest joule.

If these are the input energies, what are the sound output energies?

g) 500 J
i) 19 890 J
k) 1000 J

h) 3500 J
j) 26 080 J
l) 64 080 J

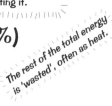

Q3 Work out the efficiency of these devices. Each one is given 10 000 J of electrical power.

You've got to decide which is the useful energy out.

a) Lamp: gives out 2100 J light, 7800 J heat.

b) Motor: gives out 6050 J sound, 3950 J kinetic energy.

c) Kettle: gives out 990 J heat to room, 9010 J heat to water.

d) Fridge: gives out 8306 J heat to room, 1694 J sound.

Give the answer to the nearest percent.

Q4 3 scientists are studying Kath's decks.

a) The scientists say the turntables are definitely either 105% or 78% efficient. How efficient must they be? How can you tell?

b) Her headphones are 50% efficient. Listening to ABBA, they waste 1000 J as heat. How much total energy does she need to supply to them?

c) A speaker gives out 50 150 J as sound, and 46 000 J as heat. A garden lamp gives out 48 484 J as heat, and 60 589 J as light. Which is more efficient?

Careful: This one's really tricky. The total energy in will be the same as the total energy out.

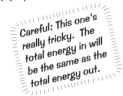

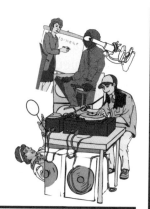

Efficiency of a teenager — zero, they don't do anything useful...

Great. This formula's pretty <u>straightforward</u>, but you need to be able to <u>flip it around</u> to work out all the different bits. You've just got to <u>learn</u> it. And watch out if you're not told the Useful Energy Out or the Total Energy In. They don't always hand it to you on a plate. That wouldn't be fun.

See p63 (Higher) or p65 (Foundation) of our Revision Guide

Efficiency

You always get Exam questions that mix up topics, so you need more than one formula. It'd only be fair for me to give you a chance to hone your skills by giving you mixed up questions myself.

Q1   A rocket chair is made, which produces energy in 3 ways.

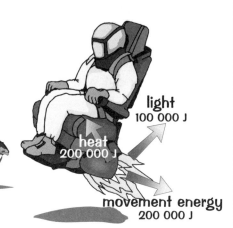

a) The diagram shows all the energy output during a test flight. What must the energy input have been?

b) How much energy is wasted by the chair?

c) What is the chair's efficiency? (to nearest 1%)

Q2   To show 5 minutes of Pets Win Pies, a TV must give out 100 500 J as light from the screen, and 52 500 J as sound from the speaker. Some energy is wasted as heat.

a) The TV is rated at 600 W. Calculate the energy it uses during 5 minutes.

You might want the formula for energy, power and time on page 8.

b) What's the efficiency of the TV?

c) How much energy would it waste if you watched 10 minutes of Who Wants To Be A Milliner?

Q3   A machine has an electric pump and a piston. It applies a pressure of 15 N/m² to the piston.

a) The pump operates at 150 W while it makes the piston move 0.1 m. It takes 6 seconds. How much energy is used?

b) The machine is 25% efficient when it moves the piston in this way. How much work is done?

c) What is the area of the piston?

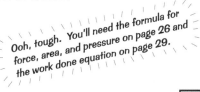

Ooh, tough. You'll need the formula for force, area, and pressure on page 26 and the work done equation on page 29.

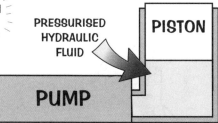

PRESSURISED HYDRAULIC FLUID

PISTON

PUMP

d) To move the piston 0.2 m, the machine uses 2000 J of electrical energy. How efficient is it now?

Inefficient, wasteful, little work done — and that's just me...

One of the nastiest mistakes here is mixing up the <u>useful</u> energy output and the <u>wasted</u> energy. Think what the machine is <u>for</u> — if a <u>heater</u> makes noise that's waste, but if a <u>speaker</u> makes noise that's useful. And watch out for questions that need <u>another formula</u> to work out the energy.

See p63 (Higher) or p65 (Foundation) of our Revision Guide

Rolling Cylinders

$$d = C \times T$$

Distance   Circumference   No. of Turns

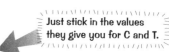

Just stick in the values they give you for C and T.

EG:
Find d if C=3 m and T=6

$$d = 3 \times 6 = 18 \, m$$

Q1 This roller's circumference is 6 m. Work out the distance it will roll if it turns these numbers of times.

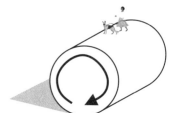

If you fully turn a cylinder with a 2 m circumference it'll have rolled for 2 m. Common sense.

a) 5 turns   e) 39 turns   i) 8.8 turns

b) 11 turns   f) 2.5 turns   j) 18 turns

c) 6 turns   g) 14 turns   k) 25 turns

d) 15 turns   h) 3 turns   l) 2 turns

Q2 Give the circumference of another roller that travels 12 m in this many turns:

a) 2 turns   e) 12 turns   i) 20 turns

b) 9 turns   f) 15 turns   j) 4 turns

c) 24 turns   g) 30 turns   k) 8 turns

d) 18 turns   h) 5 turns   l) 27 turns

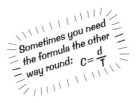

Sometimes you need the formula the other way round: $C = \dfrac{d}{T}$

Q3 Work out how many times a roller has to turn, to the nearest half turn, to travel 6 m, if its circumference is:

You'll have to rearrange the formula before you do these.

a) 5 m   d) 11 m   g) 0.75 m

b) 2 m   e) 0.6 m   h) 13 m

c) 0.4 m   f) 9 m   i) 0.25 m

Q4 From their sizes, work out the circumferences of these cylinders, and then how far (to 1 d.p.) they will roll if they make 3 turns:

Watch out: look for whether you're being given the diameter or the radius.

Use π=3.14

a) diameter 2 m   c) radius 1.6 m   e) diameter 0.5 m   g) radius 2 m

b) diameter 7 m   d) radius 11 m   f) radius 4 m   h) diameter 9 m

Q5 Work out how many turns this roller must make (to 1 d.p.) to raise the platform these distances:

Roller, circumference = 5.2 m

This is just like one of the earlier questions, but in a cunning disguise.

a) 10 m   d) 13 m   g) 6.25 m

b) 1 m   e) 4 m   h) 12 m

c) 9.5 m   f) 3 m   i) 0.5 m

Rolling cylinders — just don't inhale...

Most rolling cylinder questions are a <u>doddle</u>. Get happy swapping the formula around so you can work out <u>any bit</u>. They might try to trick you by giving you a roller with a <u>rope</u>, or only telling you the <u>diameter</u>. But, if you can get all the questions on this page right, then you'll be sorted.

Half-life

Radioactive decay is what happens when radioactive particles or gamma rays are released. One half-life is the time it takes for <u>half</u> of the radioactive atoms to decay. Knowing the half-life of something like carbon-14 can help you to work out the age of a sample.

Q1   The activity of a radio-isotope is 768 cpm. Find its activity after these numbers of half-lives:

a) One   d) Six   g) Eight

b) Three   e) Nine   h) Two

c) Five   f) Four   i) Seven

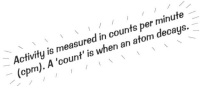
Activity is measured in counts per minute (cpm). A 'count' is when an atom decays.

Q2   The activity of a radio-isotope is 560 cpm. Two hours later it has fallen to 35 cpm.

a) Work out how many half-lives have passed.
Keep halving the initial activity until you reach the final activity.
Count how many times you need to halve the initial activity.

b) Calculate the half-life of the radio-isotope.
This is deceptively simple: you need to divide the time taken by the number of half-lives.

Q3   The activity of a radio-isotope is 7680 cpm. After 6 hours it has fallen to 30 cpm.

a) Work out how many half-lives were taken in 6 hours.

b) Calculate the half-life of the radio-isotope.

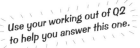
Use your working out of Q2 to help you answer this one.

Q4   Work out the half-lives of radio-isotopes with the following activities.

a)   328 cpm originally, falling to 41 cpm in 3 hours.

b)   940 cpm originally, falling to 235 cpm in 36 minutes.

c)   600 cpm originally, falling to 37.5 cpm in 25 hours.

d)   1088 cpm originally, falling to 17 cpm in 1 hour.

e)   128 cpm originally, falling to 8 cpm in 2 hours.

f)   512 cpm originally, falling to 64 cpm in a day.

<u>My cat's radioactive — it's got nine and a half lives...</u>

At first all this half-life business can seem a real pain, but it's really not too bad once you've got to grips with it. As long as you remember that the radioactivity never reaches zero, you're laughing. Repeat after me: half it and then half again and then half again and then half again and...

See p86 (Higher) or p83 (Foundation) of our Revision Guide

Half-life

Half-life questions can be tricky. It's remembering which bits to halve each time that's the trick.
Remember that half the radioactive atoms decay to non-radioactive ones each half-life.

Q1 Every three minutes, I eat <u>half</u> of the sweets I've got left. I start with a full bag of 128 sweets.

This might sound a bit daft, but it'll really help you get your head round half-lives.

    a) What is the 'half-life' of the sweets?

    b) How many sweets will I have left after 6 minutes?

    c) How many sweets will I have left after 12 minutes?

    d) How long will it take for me to have only 2 sweets left?

    e) If I'm allowed to divide each sweet up, will I ever finish all my sweets?

Q2 A wooden club is found to contain 1 part in 40 000 000 Carbon-14.

    a) Work out how many half-lives it took for this to happen.

    You need to know that the C-14 was
    originally 1 part in 10 000 000.

    b) Calculate the age of the wooden club.

    The half-life of C-14 is 5600 years.

    c) How much of the wooden club would be carbon-14 after another 5600 years?

Q3 By using the information on this page about carbon dating,
you can work out the age of this organic alien spaceship.

Assume that the amount of radioactive carbon where the spaceship came from is the same as on Earth.

    a) Work out how many half-lives have passed if the C-14
in the spaceship is now 1 part in 320 000 000.

You need to use the original activity and half-life of carbon-14, given above.

    b) Calculate the age of the spaceship.

    c) From now, how long will it take for the C-14 in the
spaceship to be 1 part in 1280 000 000?

Carbon dating — is that when you take a pencil to the cinema?...

It's very likely that you'll have to work out how old something is using radio-carbon dating in the
exam. Just remember that while the sweets from Question 1 just get eaten, the point of half-lives
is that some of the atoms stop being radioactive every half-life — the atoms don't disappear.

See p86 (Higher) or p83 (Foundation) of our Revision Guide

Combining Topics

There's nothing that examiners like better than combining different types of questions. It's really annoying, because it means that you've got to be able to spot when to use different formulas.

Q1   A 15 cm spring stretches to 20 cm when a block of metal with a mass of 4 kg hangs on it.

Use g=10 N/kg.

a) What is the downwards force due to the hanging block?

b) What would the extension of the spring be if a 6 kg mass was hanging on it?

c) The 6 kg block of metal drops off the spring, and the upwards force
    due to air resistance is 30 N. What acceleration does it have?

Q2   A woman is pushing a pram with a horizontal force of 250 N.

a) Calculate the work done if the pram is pushed a distance of 125 m.

b) Find the woman's efficiency if she uses 50 000 J of energy.

c) Work out her power output if it takes her 50 seconds to
    push the pram 125 m.

d) Work out the speed of the pram if the woman does not accelerate at all.

e) Now she speeds up to 10.5 m/s in 4 seconds. Work out the acceleration.

Q3   A diver has a mass of 55 kg.

a) How much does the diver weigh?

b) At a certain point, the force upwards due to air resistance
    is 420 N. What is the net downward force?

c) What was the diver's acceleration at this point?

d) Another diver with the same mass wears a thick swimming
    costume with a downward force of 100 N. What's the
    combined mass of the diver and her swimming costume?

e) If the force due to air resistance is the same as before,
    what is this diver's acceleration at the same point in the air?

Get formulas in the right order — sense it make more will...

Sometimes you know what two formulas you've got to use, but you haven't got a clue what order to use them in. <u>Don't</u> give up and go to the cinema instead — try it each way round. One way it should all fit together nicely, and the other won't. Obviously enough, the one that works is right.

Combining Topics

More questions on combining topics. This stuff trips up hundreds of eager GCSE physics candidates every year. But really it's just doing two straightforward questions, one after the other.

Q1   An amplifier has a resistance of 16 Ω.

a) If the amplifier runs off a 120 V supply, what is the current flowing through it?

b) What value of fuse should be used?

c) What is the power output of the amplifier?

d) Work out the amount of energy transferred by the amplifier in 2 hours.

e) Calculate the efficiency of the amplifier if the power input is 2.25 kW.

Start by working out how much energy is transferred in 2 hours by 2.25 kW.

Q2   The pole-sitting world record holder weighs 700 N
and the pole he is sitting on has a mass of 25 kg.

a) What is the combined weight of the pole-sitter and the pole?

b) The base of the pole has an area of 2.5 m². What is the pressure on the sand at the base of the pole?

c) The pole-sitter changes the base of the pole so that it now has an area of 5 m². What is the pressure now?

d) The pole will sink into the sand if the pressure is more than 475 Pa. What area of base would make the pole exert that amount of pressure?

Q3   A 20 cm long spanner is being used to loosen a nut.

a) Draw a diagram of the forces involved.

b) What is the turning moment if I use 150 N of force to push the spanner?

c) What circular distance has the end of the spanner's handle moved if it rotates the nut 4 times?

d) What is the work done by rotating the nut 4 times with a constant force of 150 N?

e) I put 910 J of energy into turning the nut. What was my efficiency?

Take a moment, force yourself, feel the pressure...

There are certain topics that examiners often shove together. Electricity stuff fits nicely into one question. Anything to do with forces can be put into one (including Hooke's Law). Energy and power often turn up hand in hand. And sometimes examiners just put random sections together...

Reading Graphs and Charts

"What on Earth are graphs doing in a book on formulas?" I hear you cry. It seemed like a good idea, given as how they come up in the exam every year.

Q1 Use the bar chart below (calm down statistics freaks, I know it's a beauty) to answer the questions. It shows the time taken for cockroaches to race 10 metres.

a) Which cockroach won the race?

b) Which cockroach was the slowest over 10 m?

c) Which cockroach came second from last?

d) How many seconds faster than Lou was Sue?

e) How many seconds difference were there between the winner and the loser at the end?

f) Which cockroaches were under the Olympic qualifying time of 59 s?

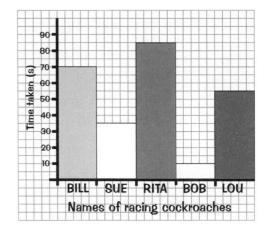

Q2 The line graph below shows the temperature of some soup as it is heated.

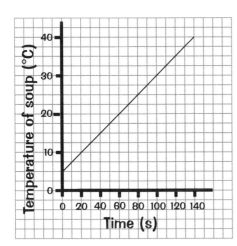

a) How hot was the soup after 20 seconds?

b) How hot was the soup after 1 minute?

c) How long did it take to heat the soup to 30 °C?

d) How long did it take to heat the soup to 40 °C?

e) By how much did the temperature rise every 20 s?

f) Assuming that this temperature rise will remain the same, what is the total time needed to heat it to 60 °C?

Q3 I asked two hundred people what pets they had. My results are displayed in this pie chart.

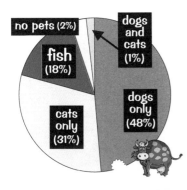

a) What percentage of people had fish?

b) What percentage of people had a dog? 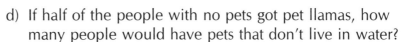 You need to look carefully at all the categories.

c) How many people only had cats?

d) If half of the people with no pets got pet llamas, how many people would have pets that don't live in water?

e) If all the people who had only cats got fish instead, how many fish owners would there be in total?

WARNING: Get ready for a load of terrible graph puns...

Graph questions can be confusing with all that information flying around. Write down all your working — even if you muddle up the answer, you still get marks if the working-out is OK. That's pretty nice of those evil examiners, next they'll be telling you they're actually human. Some chance.

Reading Graphs and Charts

These line graphs are where it all starts getting trickier. It's not just looking and then writing stuff down — this time you've got to work things out with those formulas.

Q1 A skier tucks up and starts to hurtle straight down a slope with strangely even acceleration. This velocity-time graph shows the skier's motion as she shoots down the slope.

a) What's the skier's top speed?

b) How long does it take the skier to reach top speed?

c) What's the skier's acceleration between 0 and 4 s?

d) How far did the skier travel in 4 s?

e) What was the total distance she travelled in 8 s?

f) If she weighs 55 kg what was the resultant force acting on her from
   i) 0 - 4 s and ii) 4 - 8 s?

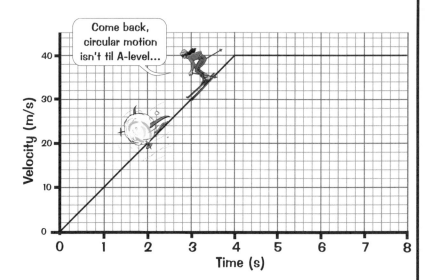

Q2 A truck travelling at 20 m/s started to slow down as it approached a traffic jam. Below is a graph showing the velocity of the truck while it was braking.

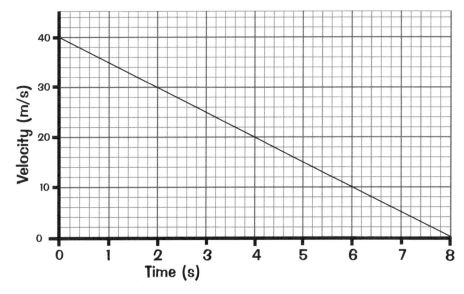

a) What is the truck's deceleration?

b) What is the braking force if the truck's mass is 1400 kg?

c) How far does the truck travel after putting the brakes on before it stops?

You've got to know that trick with the area...

d) After 4 s, if the driver brakes harder to decelerate at 10 m/s², how much quicker could the truck stop?

You don't have to do this in your head — draw on the graph if it's helpful.

e) What would the truck's stopping distance be if the deceleration was 10 m/s² for the whole journey?

Ban this page — it's too @#?!%&! graphic...

Here's a tip for you, so listen up. You are almost 100 % guaranteed to get one of these beasts in the exam. If you don't, then I'm your uncle's monkey. Figure out graphs — if you don't know your axes from your gradient you'll be heading for trouble.

See p27 (Higher) or p31 (Foundation) of our Revision Guide

Completing Graphs and Charts

You could think of these pages as "5 things to do with your favourite graph."
If you were sufficiently unusual.

Q1 Complete the bar graphs with the figures from the table and then answer the questions.

	Gargling duration (s)	Spitting distance (m)
JOHN	5	3
SHEILA	8	3.5
MARY	19	1.5
YABBA	9	4
TIM	13	4.5

I know this is gross but it wasn't my idea...

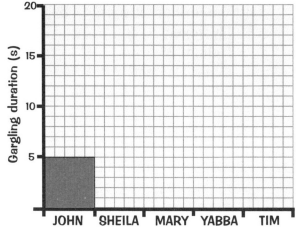

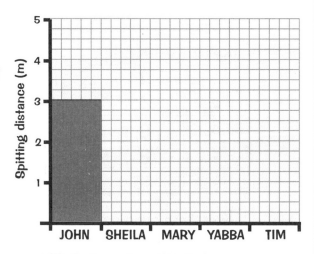

a) Who won the "distance spitting" competition?

b) Who won the "sustained gargling" competition?

c) Who came last in the spitting competition?

d) Who came last in the gargling competition?

e) 10 points were given for coming 1st in either competition, 8 points for coming 2nd, 6 points for 3rd, 4 for 4th and 2 for 5th. Write down the total number of points for each person.

Q2 Complete this pie chart with the information in the table. I'll let you guess what you have to do after that. (Hint: involves a writing implement, your brain and these questions.)

a) What percentage of the sample was graphite?

b) Which type of carbon was least common in this sample?

c) What percentage of the sample was not diamond?

Type of carbon in sample	Percentage
Coal, charcoal or soot	63
Graphite	34
Fullerenes	1
Diamond	2

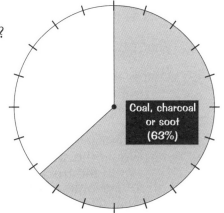

I love graphs — I'm a graphite...

This page is as easy as falling off a log. Graph and chart questions are easy marks. The exam could ask you to stick results into a graph or to look at one and work stuff out. In any case, you need to know what you're doing. You need it for coursework too — you might as well get it right.

Drawing Graphs and Charts

Graphs — you've filled them in, you've finished them off. Now it's time to get your artist's palette out and then put it away again because you don't need it and then get a pencil and a ruler to draw these graphs.

Q1 Draw and label pie charts to show this information.

This is tricky - just take your time.

a) Composition of stars:
   Hydrogen 70 %
   Helium 28 %
   Other elements 2 %

b) Domestic electricity source:
   Coal 52 %
   Oil and natural gas 16 %
   Nuclear 25 %
   Wind and Hydroelectric
                power 5 %
   Others 2 %

c) Composition of human body:
   Oxygen 65 %
   Carbon 18 %
   Hydrogen 10 %
   Nitrogen 3 %
   Calcium 2 %
   Others 2 %

Q2 Draw bar graphs or line graphs for the information below. The first two say which type of graph to use. For the third one, choose the best type.

a) Draw a line graph to show this skateboarder's distance with time.

Time (s)	Distance (m)
1	2
2	4
3	6
4	8
5	10

b) Display these weights on a bar graph.

	Weight (kg)
Bobby	80
Sarah	50
Jazza	60
Billwonk	75

c) Show this rollercoaster's speed with time on a graph.

Time (s)	Speed (m/s)
0	0
10	8
20	16
30	24
40	32

These might seem too easy, but you need to practise doing them without making silly mistakes.

Q3 Answer these questions using the information above and the graphs you drew.

a) What is the speed of the skateboarder?

b) If 50 % of all the carbon in the body is Carbon-14, what percentage of the whole body is Carbon-14?

c) What is the acceleration of the rollercoaster?

d) What percentage of domestic electricity is supplied by coal, oil or natural gas?

e) What is the average weight of the four people in Q2 b)?

f) What distance has the skateboarder travelled in 4.5 s?

Look back to page 13 if you've not got the formula stuffed into your brain yet...

g) If the rollercoaster carried on at the same acceleration, what would the speed be after 70 s?

h) If all four people in Q2 b) were on the accelerating rollercoaster, which has a mass of 275 kg, what would be the resultant force on the rollercoaster?

You'll get so quick — everyone will want your autograph...

Take extra care drawing graphs in exams. You'll get questions about it so make your life easy — do the job properly. These questions allow you to really show them you know what you're doing. Oh, and whatever you do, don't forget your ruler and pencil. Wibbly biro won't impress anyone.

Drawing Graphs and Charts

This page is where it all gets hard. You've got to draw precise graphs, remember formulas <u>and</u> work out answers all in the same question. Ick.

Time (mins)	Counts per minute
0	11 000
15	8200
30	5900
45	4450
60	3500
75	2600
90	1900
105	1400
120	1000
135	750
150	550
165	400

Q1 A physicist wants to find the half-life of a sample of metal. She records the counts per minute over several hours. The large table shows her results.

a) Plot a graph of her results. Put time on the horizontal axis and draw a smooth curve through the points.

Metal	Half-life
Ag-108	2.4 mins
Ag-110	24.6 secs
In-117	44 mins
Pb-211	36.1 mins
Pb-214	27 mins

b) What is the half-life of the metal sample (to nearest minute)?

c) Use the table of metal half-lives to identify the sample.

Q2 A coach has its speed limited so that it cannot exceed 50 mph.

Time (s)	Velocity (m/s)
0	0
2	5
4	10
6	15
8	20
10	22
12	22
14	22

a) Plot a velocity–time graph for the data in the table.

b) What is the coach's top speed in metres per second? Draw an arrow on your graph to show where the coach reaches this speed.

c) What is the acceleration of the coach from 0 to 8 seconds?

d) If the coach has mass 6500 kg, what resultant force acts on the coach during this time?

e) Estimate how far the coach travelled in the 14 seconds to the nearest 5 metres.

Q3 An electronics engineer has two mystery components. He records current through the components at different voltages.

Voltage (V)	Component 1 Current (A)	Component 2 Current (A)
-4	-2	0
-2	-1	0
0	0	0
2	1	0.3
4	2	1
6	3	2.7
8	4	5
10	5	10

a) Plot these two sets of data on the same axes.

b) Identify the components and label them on your graph.

Look at page 4 of The Revision Guide for help.

c) Which component obeys Ohm's Law? What is its resistance?

Q4 A rusty old Beetle leaks oil at the rate of one drop every second. The diagram below shows drops of oil on a stretch of road where the car was changing speed. The scale underneath is in metres.

a) How long did the car take to travel the 76 m shown in the picture?

b) How far had the car travelled after four seconds?

c) What was the average velocity over the whole trip (to 1 d.p.)?

d) Draw a blue line on the picture to show where the car had constant speed.

e) What was the maximum acceleration? Draw a red line to show where this occurred.

f) What resultant force acts on the car at this acceleration if it weighs 975 kg?

~~a graph a minute...~~ ~~graph-t it on...~~ ~~I saw a graph in the zoo...~~

Congratulations on surviving to the end of the page. And it's the end of the book as well.
Just when you were really starting to enjoy yourself, ahh well. If you're after that good grade, get
lots of practice in before the exams. It's up to you now — go forth and multiply (and divide).

PMW40

Page 4 Electrical Power
Q1 a) 18 W b) 16 W c) 27 W d) 9 W e) 2.4 W
f) 16.8 W g) 22.5 W h) 5 W i) 51.3 W
Q2 a) 5 V b) 2.5 V c) 20 V d) 500 V e) 2.25 V
f) 50 V g) 1250 V h) 625 V i) 37.5 V
Q3 a) 50 A b) 2000 A c) 2000 A d) 60 A e) 4500 A
f) 12.5 A g) 110 A h) 800 A i) 400 A
Q4 a) 1380 A b) 1058 A c) 10 A d) 13 A

Page 5 Electrical Power
Q1 a) 150 V b) 125 V c) 250 V d) 2.5 A so use a 3 A fuse.
Q2 a) 1196 W b) 1403 W c) 3 A fuse d) 13 A fuse e) 800 W f) 2.5 A
Q3 a) 24 A b) 120 V c) 30 A fuse d) 40 A fuse

Page 6 Resistance
Q1 a) 2 Ω b) 4 Ω c) 3 Ω d) 1 Ω e) 6 Ω f) 3 Ω
g) 4.5 Ω h) 0.25 Ω i) 0.5 Ω
Q2 a) 6 V b) 10 V c) 16 V d) 18 V e) 2 V f) 9 V
g) 4.5 V h) 3 V i) 12 V
Q3 a) 2 A b) 3 A c) 3 A d) 2 A e) 3 A f) 1 A g) 0.5 A
h) 0.25 A i) 0.6 A
Q4 a) 5 Ω b) 2.4 A Q5 a) 46 A b) 24 A

Page 7 Resistance
Q1 a) 24 Ω b) 15 Ω c) 5 A
Q2 a) 12 Ω b) 2 A c) 6 V d) 19.1 A
Q3 a) 12.8 A b) 1.7 A c) 27 V d) 35.4 Ω

Page 8 Energy in Kilowatt-hours
Q1 a) 6 kWh b) 12 kWh c) 24 kWh d) 5 kWh
e) 3 kWh f) 15 kWh g) 48 kWh h) 0.3 kWh i) 0.2 kWh
Q2 a) 2 kW b) 3 kW c) 8 kW d) 0.5 kW e) 1.5 kW
f) 0.75 kW g) 11.5 kW h) 22.5 kW i) 1.2 kW
Q3 a) 1 h b) 3 h c) 6 h d) 0.5 h or 30 mins
e) 0.25 h or 15 mins f) 0.75 h or 45 mins
g) 2 h h) 12 h i) 0.06 h or 3.6 mins
Q4 a) 105 kWh b) 7.5 kWh c) ²/₃ hr or 40 mins d) 24 kW

Page 9 Cost of Electricity
Q1 a) £7.50 b) £75 c) £6.75 d) £11.25 e) £37.50
f) £120 g) £38.70 h) £74.85 i) £2595.90
Q2 a) 10 units b) 20 units c) 200 units d) 1000 units e) 562.5 units
f) 6250 units g) 9375 units h) 647.5 units i) 9465 units
Q3 a) 7 p b) 14 p c) 10 p d) 9.3 p e) 10.8 p
f) 12.7 p g) 8.5 p h) 12.2 p i) 11.1 p
Q4 a) 1682.1 units b) £134.57 c) 2625 units d) 6.5 p

Page 10 Energy and Cost
Q1 a) 4 h b) 26.25 kWh c) 1½ h extra
Q2 a) 13.5 kWh b) 3.5 h c) 6 p
Q3 a) 75 mins b) 5 kWh c) 45 p d) £2.03

Page 11 Force and Motion
Q1 a) 50 N b) 35 N c) 376 N d) 2.3 N e) 2.1 N
f) 220.4 N g) 253.3 N h) 8411.6 N i) 5.3 N
Q2 a) 20 m/s² b) 5 m/s² c) 14 m/s² d) 6.4 m/s² e) 0.3 m/s²
f) 6.3 m/s² g) 28 m/s² h) 3.9 m/s² i) 29.8 m/s²
Q3 a) 10 kg b) 8 kg c) 38.3 kg d) 2.5 kg e) 5.7 kg
f) 18.4 kg g) 65 kg h) 5.9 kg i) 15 kg
Q4 a) 3600 N b) 25.2 N c) 918 N d) 321.6 N
e) 0.02 N f) 475.39 N g) 794.61 N

Page 12 Force and Motion
Q1 a) Rock b) Mini c) Skier d) Motorbike
e) Sky-diver f) Magpie g) Horse
Q2 a) 5 m/s² b) 4 m/s² c) 5 m/s² d) -8 m/s²
e) 0.6 m/s² f) 0.5 m/s² g) 4.2 m/s² h) 0.5 m/s²
Q3 a) 73.5 N b) 631 N c) 45 kg d) 58.8 N
e) 5.4 m/s² f) 6.6 kg, to thief.

Page 13 Force and Motion
Q1 a) 2.5 m/s² b) Less push or more weight in tractor.
c) 43 N d) No; no forces and so no deceleration.
Q2 a) 96 N b) 825 N c) 267
Q3 a) 6000 N b) 6000 N c) 2820 N in direct. of accel.
d) 3020 N e) 2875, 4.6 m/s²

Page 14 Mass and Weight
Q1 a) 50 N b) 100 N c) 2270 N d) 325 N e) 5 N
f) 35 N g) 3 N h) 2315 N i) 2.5 N
Q2 a) 0.6 kg b) 0.8 kg c) 14.3 kg d) 5 kg e) 32 kg
f) 0.2 kg g) 3.4 kg h) 25.4 kg i) 0.05 kg
Q3 a) 8 N b) 16 N c) 363.2 N d) 52 N e) 0.8 N
f) 5.6 N g) 0.48 N h) 370.4 N i) 0.4 N
Q4 a) Moon – g – 1.6 N/kg b) i) 650 N   ii) 104 N
c) i) 800 N ii) 128 N d) 5 kg e) 900 N

Page 15 Mass and Weight
Q1 a) 800 N b) 130 N c) 1.625 m/s²
Q2 a) 54.6 kg b) 1226 N c) 109.2 N
Q3 a) 41.7 kg b) 1250 N c) 833 N d) 437.5 N

Page 16 Speed and Velocity
Q1 a) 10 m/s b) 15 m/s c) 20 m/s d) 5 m/s e) 8.3 m/s
f) 20.5 m/s g) 20 m/s h) 12.5 m/s i) 8.3 m/s
Q2 a) 300 m b) 400 m c) 200 m d) 420 m
e) 2160 m f) 350 m g) 18000 m h) 8.3 km i) 60 km
Q3 a) 0.5 s b) 5 s c) 25 s d) 30 s e) 3.3 s f) 78.6 s
g) 30 mins h) 41.6 mins i) 125 s
Q4 a) 1.1 m/s b) 0.2 cm/s c) 13.3 m/s d) 16.7 m/s
e) 2.1 m/s f) 26.7 m/s g) 0.6 m/s h) 6.7 m/s i) 2000 m/s

Page 17 Speed and Velocity
Q1 a) 110.8 km/h b) 0 km/h c) 2 mins 24 s d) 180 km/h
Q2 a) Yes. b) 1134.3 km/h NE c) 53.5 mins d) No.
Q3 a) 3.3 m/s E b) 12 mins c) 90 s (twice as fast)
d) 4.8 m/s e) 2.2 mins

Page 18 Acceleration
Q1 a) 0.5 m/s² b) 2.5 m/s² c) 4 m/s² d) 2 m/s²
e) 0.8 m/s² f) 4.5 m/s² g) 1.3 m/s² h) 0.3 m/s²
i) 18.7 m/s² j) 18.4 m/s²
Q2 a) 2 s b) 6 s c) 9 s d) 6.4 s e) 4.3 s f) 5 s
g) 1.0 s h) 1.6 s i) 2.2 s j) 0.1 s
Q3 a) 0.05 m/s² b) 4 m/s² c) 0.05 m/s² d) 6.1 m/s²
e) 5.1 s f) 5 s g) 5.6 s h) 11.1 m/s²
i) 16.7 m/s (or 60 km/h); 50 m

Page 19 Velocity and Acceleration
Q1 a) 1388.9 m/s b) 2.5 h c) 142.9 m/s²
Q2 a) 112.6 b) 60 mph 96.6 km/h c) 93.3 mph No! d) 2.1 m/s²
Q3 a) 4 km b) 3.6 m/s c) 6.1 m/s d) 0.1 s e) 5940 m; further.

Page 20 Waves
Q1 a) 0.1 Hz b) 0.2 Hz c) 0.25 Hz d) 0.5 Hz
e) 0.05 Hz f) 1 Hz g) 5 Hz h) 100 Hz
Q2 a) 0.05 s b) 0.5 s c) 10 s d) 0.001 s
e) 0.004 s f) 0.25 s g) 500 s h) 0.008 s
Q3 a) 24 m/s b) 60 m/s c) 120 m/s d) 240 m/s e) 12 m/s
f) 6 m/s g) 12000 m/s h) 96 m/s i) 14.4 m/s
Q4 a) 3 m b) 4 m c) 10 m d) 0.03 m e) 250 m
f) 0.02 m g) 5 m h) 2 m i) 0.1 m
Q5 a) 2 m/s b) 2.4 m/s c) 0.25 m/s

Page 21 Waves
Q1 a) 0.5 Hz b) 10 m c) 1 m – 6 m/s, 4 m – 3.5 m,
3 m – 6 m/s, 2 m – 12.5 Hz d) 4m
Q2 a) 900 m/s b) 6.67 cm c) 200 kHz
Q3 a) 3.001 × 10⁸ m/s b) 4.007 × 10¹⁴ Hz

Page 22 Moments
Q1 a) 6 Nm Anti-CW b) 28 Nm CW c) 60 Nm CW
d) 51.84 Nm Anti-CW
Q2 a) CW 9 Nm, Anti-CW 15 Nm, tip left.
b) CW 34.5 Nm, Anti-CW 67.5 Nm, tip left.
c) CW 55.2 Nm, Anti-CW 9.2 Nm ,tip right.
d) CW 6.8 Nm, Anti-CW 6.58 Nm ,tip right.
e) CW 6 Nm, Anti-CW 6 Nm, balance.
f) CW 48 Nm, Anti-CW 25 Nm, tip right.
Q3 a) 10 N b) 20 Nm CW c) Cat goes down d) 1 m left of pivot.

Page 23 Moments
Q1 a) 32.5 Nm b) 13 N c) 300 N
Q2 a) 300 N b) 600 N c) 224 N d) Yes
Q3 a) Mom only 3 Nm b) 35.1 N c) 23.5 N d) Max dist; min force.

Page 24 Hooke's Law
Q1 a) 6 cm b) 9 cm c) 0.75 cm d) 2.25 cm e) 6.75 cm
f) 9.75 cm g) 10.5 cm h) 4.13 cm i) 5.63 cm
Q2 a) 10 N b) 1 N c) 4 N d) 2.5 N e) 7.5 N
f) 6.5 N g) 8.5 N h) 4.75 N i) 0.75 N
Q3 a) 20 cm b) 25 cm c) 12.5 cm d) 17.5 cm e) 11.3 cm
f) 27.5 cm g) 26.3 cm h) 18.8 cm i) 32.5 cm
Q4 a) 800 g b) 1200 g c) 1030 g d) 0 g e) 86 g
f) 886 g g) 1290 g h) 1160 g i) 383 g
Q5 a) 15.6 cm b) 20.3 cm c) 36.8 cm d) 25.8 cm
e) 34.8 cm f) 22.8 cm g) 11.9 cm h) 29.1 cm i) 40.9 cm

Page 25 Hooke's Law
Q1 a)

b) The extension stops being proportional to the load.
c) 12 cm/N
d) 2.58 N
e) 62.8 cm
f) 30 cm
Q2 a) 58 cm b) 1 cm/N c) 40 cm d) 90 cm
Q3 a) 41.4 cm b) 7 monkeys c) 34 monkeys.

Page 26 Pressure = Force ÷ Area
Q1 a) 3500 Pa b) 1167 Pa c) 1400 Pa d) 2333 Pa
e) 1458 Pa f) 5000 Pa g) 1842 Pa h) 8750 Pa i) 2917 Pa
Q2 a) 1 m² b) 2.6 m² c) 0.76 m² d) 0.1 m² e) 0.25 m²
f) 0.16 m² g) 6.5 m² h) 1.04 m² i) 0.47 m²
Q3 a) 117 N/cm² b) 23.3 N/cm² c) 66.7 N/cm² d) 46.7 N/cm²
e) 25.9 N/cm² f) 31.1 N/cm² g) 21.2 N/cm² h) 54.3 N/cm²
i) 41.7 N/cm²
Q4 a) 693 Pa b) 320 Pa c) 240 Pa d) 440 Pa e) 520 Pa
f) 120 Pa g) 220 Pa h) 367 Pa i) 593 Pa
Q5 a) 4444 Pa b) 3636 Pa c) 1739 Pa d) 2222 Pa
e) 1818 Pa f) 2667 Pa g) 2105 Pa h) 2000 Pa i) 2286 Pa

Page 27 Pressure and Hydraulics
Q1 a) 120 N/cm² b) 7200 N c) 12 times
Q2 a) 8400 N b) 1200 N c) 3000 N d) 2100 N
e) 3900 N f) 4860 N g) 10236 N h) 564 N i) 7608 N
Q3 a) 9.3 N/cm² b) 2474 N c) 6.2 times d) 5 gorillas
Q4 a) 1125 N b) 1624 N c) 2460 N d) 390 N
e) 1034 N f) 956 N g) 701 N h) 1200 N

Page 28 Pressure = Force ÷ Area
Q1   Chris a) 650 N, b) 1.08 N/cm²   c) The pressure
Simah a) 500 N, b) 1.56 N/cm²   would be doubled.
Steve a) 750 N, b) 1.17 N/cm²   d) Simah
Pam a) 600 N, b) 1.36 N/cm²   e) Wear shoes with a
Sheetal a) 550 N, b) 1.38 N/cm²   smaller sole area,
Iain a) 700 N, b) 1.13 N/cm²   e.g. women's shoes.
Q2 a) 560 Pa b) 1360 Pa c) 36 N d) No
Q3 a) 143 N/cm² b) 12 N/cm² c) 2.37 N/cm² d) 22.5 N/cm²

Page 29 Work Done = Force × Distance
Q1 a) 5 kJ b) 25 J c) 1.25 kJ d) 21.5 kJ e) 100 kJ
f) 3.65 kJ g) 8.85 kJ h) 67.75 kJ i) 49.325 kJ
Q2 a) 50 J b) 300 J c) 275 J d) 100 J e) 600 J
f) 375 J g) 175 J h) 525 J i) 475 J
Q3 a) 3.9 kJ b) 2.775 kJ c) 5.025 kJ d) 1.8 kJ e) 3.45 kJ
f) 5.175 kJ g) 1.575 kJ h) 4.125 kJ i) 5.475 kJ
Q4 a) 1.5 kJ b) 1600 kJ c) 100 kJ d) 2 J e) 10 kJ
f) 180 kJ g) 4.9 kJ h) 40 kJ

Page 30 Work Done = Force × Distance
Q1 a) 1800 kJ b) 2380 kJ c) 1600 kJ
Q2 a) 6 kJ b) 5.4 kJ c) 7.8 kJ d) 27
Q3 a) 36 kJ b) 208 kJ c) 30.6 m d) 20.25 kJ each

Page 31 Power = Work ÷ Time
Q1 a) 5000 W b) 2083 W c) 1667 W d) 1754 W
e) 2564 W f) 2326 W g) 2299 W h) 1912 W i) 3040 W
Q2 a) 1111 W b) 2222 W c) 1944 W d) 833 W
e) 972 W f) 1250 W g) 1756 W h) 1428 W i) 2217 W
Q3 a) 16.7 W b) 50 W c) 33.3 W d) 66.7 W e) 21.1 W
f) 17.4 W g) 74.1 W h) 37.7 W i) 25.3 W
Q4 a) 208 s b) 42 s c) 146 s d) 354 s e) 398 s
f) 477 s g) 547 s h) 324 s i) 205 s
Q5 a) 60 kJ b) 72 kJ c) 96 kJ d) 48 kJ e) 57 kJ
f) 87 kJ g) 109.5 kJ h) 64.5 kJ i) 82.5 kJ

Page 32 Work Done = Force × Distance
Q1 a) 286 W b) 222 W c) 1 hour d) 220 W e) 44%
Q2 a) 75 W b) 35 W c) 50 W d) 60 times
Q3 a) 3733 W b) 2273 W c) 1067 W d) 8 mins 20 secs

Page 33 Efficiency
Q1 a) 0.53 b) 0.7 c) 0.26 d) 0.32 e) 0.1 f) 0.2
g) 0.52 h) 0.53 i) 0.85
Q2 a) 86% b) 14% c) 98% d) 1% e) 40% f) 71% g) 89%
h) 81% i) 22%
Q3 a) 11980 J b) 7047 J c) 23960 J d) 59900 J e) 8557 J
f) 17114 J g) 14610 J h) 6656 J
Q4 a) 60 J b) 150 J c) 3000 J d) 204 J e) 486 J f) 414 J
Q5 a) 16000 J, 80%, b) 17200 J, 86%, c) 9000 J 45% d) 15750 J, 79%

Page 34 Efficiency
Q1 a) 40% b) 18% c) 36% d) 63% e) 10%
f) 14% g) 59% h) 25% i) 72%
Q2 a) 5714 J b) 11571 J c) 763 J d) 25429 J
e) 21437 J f) 31114 J g) 175 J h) 1225 J
i) 6961.5 J j) 9128 J k) 350 J l) 22428 J
Q3 a) 21% b) 40% c) 90% d) 83%
Q4 a) 78% – 100% not possible. b) 2000 J c) Garden lamp

Page 35 Efficiency
Q1 a) 500 000 J b) 300 000 J c) 40%   Q3 a) 900 J b) 225 J
Q2 a) 180 000 J b) 85% c) 54 000 J   c) 150 m² d) 23%

Page 36 Rolling Cylinders
Q1 a) 30 m b) 66 m c) 36 m d) 90 m e) 234 m f) 15 m
g) 84 m h) 18 m i) 52.8 m j) 108 m k) 150 m l) 12 m
Q2 a) 6 m b) 1.3 m c) 0.5 m d) 0.7 m e) 1 m f) 0.8 m
g) 0.4 m h) 2.4 m i) 0.6 m j) 3 m k) 1.5 m l) 0.4 m
Q3 a) 1 b) 3 c) 15 d) 0.5 e) 10 f) 0.5 g) 8 h) 0.5 i) 24
Q4 a) 18.8 m b) 65.9 m c) 30.1 m d) 207.2 m e) 4.7 m
f) 75.4 m g) 37.7 m h) 84.8 m
Q5 a) 1.9 b) 0.2 c) 1.8 d) 2.5 e) 0.8 f) 0.6 g) 1.2 h) 2.3 i) 0.1

Page 37 Half-Life
Q1 a) 384 cpm b) 96 cpm c) 24 cpm d) 12 cpm e) 1.5 cpm
f) 48 cpm g) 3 cpm h) 192 cpm i) 6 cpm
Q2 a) 4 half-lives b) 0.5 h   Q3 a) 8 half-lives b) 0.75 h
Q4 a) 1 h b) 18 mins c) 6.25 h d) 10 mins e) 0.5 h f) 8 h

Page 38 Half-life
Q1 a) 3 mins b) 32 sweets c) 8 sweets d) 18 mins e) No
Q2 a) 2 half-lives b) 11 200 years c) 1 part in 80 000 000
Q3 a) 5 half-lives b) 28 000 years c) 11200 years

Page 39 Combining Topics
Q1 a) 40 N b) 7.5 cm c) 5 m/s²
Q2 a) 31250 J b) 62.5% c) 625 W d) 2.5 m/s e) 2 m/s²
Q3 a) 550 N. b) 130 N c) 2.36 m/s² (2dp) d) 65 kg e) 3.54 m/s²

Page 40 Combining Topics
Q1 a) 7.5 A b) 10 A c) 900 W d) 6480 kJ e) 40%
Q2 a) 950 N b) 380 Pa c) 190 Pa d) 2 m²
Q3 a) [Force diagram, 20 cm] b) 30 Nm c) 5.024 m d) 753.6 J e) 82.8%

Page 41 Reading Graphs and Charts
Q1 a) Bob b) Rita c) Bill d) 20 s e) 75 s f) Sue, Bob, Lou
Q2 a) 10°C b) 20°C c) 100 s d) 140 s e) 5°C f) 220 s
Q3 a) 18% b) 49 % c) 62 people d) 162 people e) 98 people

Page 42 Reading Graphs and Charts
Q1 a) 40 m/s b) 4 s c) 10 m/s² d) 80 m e) 240 m f) i)550 N,ii)0 N
Q2 a) 5 m/s² b) 7000 m c) 160 m d) 2 s quicker e) 80 m

Page 43 Completing Graphs and Charts

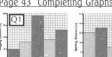

Q1 a) Tim b) Mary c) Mary
d) John e) John 6, Sheila10,
Mary 12, Yabba 14, Tim 18

Q2 a) 34%
b) Fullerenes
c) 98%

Page 44 Drawing Graphs and Charts

Q3 a) 2 m/s b) 9% c) 0.8 m/s d) 68%
e) 66.25 kg f) 9 m g) 56 m/s h) 432 N

Page 45 Drawing Graphs and Charts
Q1   b) 36 mins   Q2   a) 22 m/s c) 2.5 m/s²
c) Lead Pb-211   d) 16 250 N e) 210 m

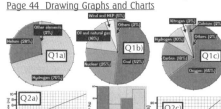

Q3   b) Component 1 — Resistor
Component 2 — Diode
c) Component 1 obeys Ohm's
Law. Resistance 2 Ω.
Q4   a) 9 s b) 23 m c) 8.4 m/s
e) 2 m/s² f) 1950 N